About the Author

With thirty years' experience and numerous qualifications in alternative and complementary medicine, Keith Mason runs his own radionic and clinical practice in Hampshire, England, treating patients both locally and worldwide. He uses radionics as his primary method of diagnosis and treatments including homeopathy, element therapy (base mineral elements given as medication), biochemistry, herbal medicine and Bach Flower Remedies.

Over the past fifteen years Keith has developed a dynamic and accurate assessment technique based on specialised radionic analysis and treatment instruments, that eliminates the need for face-to-face consultations. Patients unable to visit the practice submit a completed case history and a hair sample. The results of the radionic analysis and assessment, which aim to establish the cause of their symptoms, are then sent by mail, fax or e-mail directly to the patient.

Keith is an adviser on energy medicine to the Institute for Complementary Medicine in London and lectures extensively around the world. He has written three other books including *Radionics and Progressive Energies* and *Medicine for the 21st Century*. His latest book, published by Piatkus, is entitled *Thoughts that Harm, Thoughts that Heal*.

The Radionics handbook

The
Radionics
handbook

How to analyse your health and enhance your wellbeing

Keith Mason

PIATKUS

This book is for Guy Pilbeam who stalwartly
supports energy medicine and radionics.
Guy, I dedicate this book to you with my thanks.

Published in the UK in 2001 by
Judy Piatkus (Publishers) Limited
5 Windmill Street
London W1T 2JA
e-mail: info@piatkus.co.uk

For the latest news and information on all our titles,
visit our website at www.piatkus.co.uk

A catalogue record for this book is available
from the British Library

ISBN 0 7499 2120 X

This book has been printed on paper manufactured with
respect for the environment using wood from managed
sustainable resources

Typeset by Action Publishing Technology Ltd, Gloucester
Printed and bound in Great Britain by
Biddles Ltd, Guildford and King's Lynn
www.biddles.co.uk

Contents

Acknowledgements

In my thirty years of radionic practice, I have met numerous practitioners around the world who have played a unique role in the development and enhancement of radionics and energy medicine. However, two men have played a significant role in the development and acceptance of complementary medicine and have steadfastly supported radionics and energy medicine in particular for the last two decades.

Anthony Baird and **Michael Endacott**, directors of the Institute for Complementary Medicine, have placed energy medicine and radionics towards the forefront of complementary medicine for the twenty-first century. They have quietly laboured from the halls of parliament and the corridors of the health service to radio and television chat shows, spreading the truth about complementary medicine's role in the healthcare of the public. I acknowledge them for their continuing endeavours and aspirations to introduce total professionalism and the highest academic standards in complementary medicine and to generate an appreciation by the general public, but especially for their commitment to the betterment of the nation's health and its understanding of spiritual values.

Introduction

How does radionics differ from other alternative and complementary therapies?

- It's a healing therapy for which you do not have to visit the practitioner.

- When you are registered with a radionic practitioner you can be on the other side of the earth and still receive your treatment.

- The twenty-first century is the age of electronic communication, it's the age of the Internet, it's the age of radionics – the energy medicine of the future.

These are some of the reasons why radionics may well be the therapy for you. It's the only way to have your health assessed, and even get treatment for your symptoms, at a distance. Sounds too good to be true? Well it's actually nothing new; it all started in the early twentieth century when an eminent American neurologist, Dr Albert Abrams, detected electromagnetic signals being emitted from diseased tissue. As the years passed, Abrams and many of his conventional medical colleagues studied this phenomenon. Their research on the electromagnetic fields that emanated from living and diseased tissue culminated in a diagnostic system which became the forerunner of modern radionics.

THE BEGINNINGS OF RADIONICS

The experiments carried out by Abrams and his colleagues in the early part of the twentieth century were performed directly on patients. However, later experiments, particularly those conducted by Dr Ruth Drown (an eminent chiropractor, also in the USA), showed that the same signals could be detected in a blood or tissue sample that had been removed from the patient. The person's state of health could be assessed from the sample provided, just as blood and tissue samples are tested in a laboratory.

Nothing extraordinary here, you may think. However, all those years ago, there was a major breakthrough in the understanding of electromagnetic energy, its subtle abilities and the way it behaved. They found that the practitioner could diagnose the ailment from a blood or tissue sample. But, even more extraordinary, the practitioner could *treat* the patient by treating the sample. And it made no difference how far away the patient was.

By using the sample taken from the patient, and correcting or manipulating his or her electrical fields with radionic instruments, the illness could be treated no matter where that patient was in the world. This was the beginning of radionics. Chapter 2 charts the evolution of this amazing therapy, from the 1920s right up to the present, showing how eighty years of research and practice have placed radionics at the forefront of energy medicine for the twenty-first century.

THE 'WHITE WITCH DOCTOR' OF CONSTANTIA

My own personal interest in radionics started in 1967 when I was lucky enough to be living under the granite gaze of the great Table Mountain in the beautiful Cape of Good Hope in South Africa (having emigrated from England in the early 1960s). In Cape Town I began my classical homeopathic and naturopathic training and eventually established a healing practice, working from my home situated amongst the leafy glades and vineyards of Constantia. I had never heard of radionics, even when studying classical homeopathy, until my first son Richard was diagnosed with chronic asthma when he was eighteen months old. Conventional and even homeopathic medicine could do no more than relieve the symptoms, but then my African gardener suggested I see a lady he affectionately called, the 'white witch doctor' of Constantia.

Initially I took little notice of his advice and relied totally upon orthodox medical opinion, drug treatment and continual steaming to aid Richard's breathing, which he of course found most distressing as a little boy. Richard deteriorated considerably, conventional medicine could do no more, and so I finally searched out the white witch doctor named Sheila Toms that my gardener had recommended.

For the initial consultation I took Richard on my own. We were invited into Sheila's elegant and beautiful home and then taken into a room where the walls were festooned with shelf upon shelf of little bottles containing tiny white tablets. Other, more substantial shelves held ominous black instruments displaying rows of numbered dials. The room resembled that of a ham radio operator who indulged in chemistry as a hobby! As I gazed around the room, I was suddenly aware that silence had descended; Sheila was waiting for my reply to a question she had asked. I apologised for my vagueness and began explaining Richard's case in some detail and our lack of success in using orthodox medicine to treat him.

I watched doubtfully as Sheila took Richard from me, held him in one arm and walked around the room, touching little bottles with her other hand from which dangled a string or cord with something on the end. This 'something' (which resembled a small builder's plumb line) would oscillate, then suddenly become still, then swing violently in another direction, then stop. I was totally confused when she took a small bottle of tiny pillules off a shelf, placed them on a metal plate on one of the radio-like instruments, and proceeded to twiddle a few of the numbered dials.

Then, to my astonishment, she sat Richard down, took a pair of scissors, removed a small snippet of hair from the nape of his neck, and placed the hair between two sticky labels. This she placed next to the little bottle, then she twiddled some of the numbered dials again whilst 'the something' in her hand swung around violently, before settling into a rhythmic swing.

Satisfied, she gave Richard back to me, along with the little bottle of pillules and said, 'Give him a dose of three little pills night and morning and I will treat him every day for a month.'

'What time tomorrow then?' I asked.

'I need only see him in a month's time,' said Sheila.

Still in my vague state, Richard and I left, after placing a little something in the donation plate by the door on our way out. I was now even more confused and bewildered. What on earth had she meant when she said, 'I will treat him every day, but bring him back in a month's time'? Perplexed, I drove home with Richard, and placed the pills she had given me in a little-used drawer.

The next day Richard's breathing deteriorated yet again, the doctor came, and a hospital admission was arranged for the following day. I was becoming very alarmed. That evening I opened the forgotten drawer and looked apprehensively at the mysterious little bottle. What should I do? What was there to lose? That evening I placed three of the tiny pillules inside Richard's mouth. The night passed without the usual bedside steaming to assist his breathing. The morning dawned with Richard asking for something to eat and after he had a little food I gave him three more pills from the bottle. By lunchtime his breathing was deeper and less laboured. Just twenty-four hours after our visit to the white witch doctor, something was changing.

I cancelled the hospital admission, much to the doctor's consternation, and after one week of little magic pills I called Sheila to give a report on Richard's progress. Before I could say anything much she informed me that the readings for the respiration had improved dramatically and 'the activity of the inherent miasmic trait' (whatever that was supposed to mean) was less, and she was so pleased Richard was improving. I found her comments baffling, but of course she was right. Richard *was* improving, yet she had not laid eyes on him since our initial meeting a week before.

She said she had been treating him daily via his hair sample, and the Arsenicum Album pills were working, and this treatment should be continued to the end of the month. This was done and, by the end of two months and two more consultations, Richard was becoming an active and healthy little boy.

This was my first taste of what I now know to be the science of radionics or, as Sheila Toms practised it, the art of medical radiesthesia. To me this was a miracle; my son had been cured of an illness for which orthodox medicine could only ease the symptoms but certainly not provide a cure. This event was a watershed in my career, and the start of a journey towards understanding the subtle energies of humanity as well as gaining a broader insight into the world of nature in which we live. For this I have to thank a wise old African named Cornelius Mbele, who has now in all probability left this earth. It was he who witnessed Richard's inability to breathe when he was out in the garden, and it was he who told me about a white witch doctor – the extraordinary Mrs Toms.

MEETINGS WITH REMARKABLE MEN

So this was the beginning of my years of radionic study. In those early days I came across the works of Dr Aubrey Westlake and it was his book, *The Pattern of Health*, that introduced me to the history and medical background of radionics. I returned to England on numerous occasions, spending time in the company of this remarkable man, learning more from him about the subtle, spiritual energies of the human form.

During my regular visits to Aubrey he introduced me to the writer and distinguished radionic practitioner David Tansley and the eminent radionic practitioner Malcolm Rae, researcher and developer of the most amazing radionic instruments. I spent many hours studying with Malcolm, and his instruments found their way back to Cape Town to further treat those of my patients who were already on classical homeopathic treatment. (I had discovered that radionic instruments could also simulate or alter the energies contained in conventional homeopathic remedies. Using these radionic instruments, one could not only treat patients in their absence but make up remedies for them to take orally.)

The results I obtained from these instruments astounded me, as they did my patients. I was hooked. So much so that radionics became my principal diagnostic tool. Returning to England for good in 1979, I continued my research on the work of Malcolm Rae after his untimely death in the same year.

RADIONICS TODAY

Radionics has made enormous progress, both in its methods of treatment and its underlying philosophy. Chapter 3 describes these advances and explains how modern radionics is linked with the theories of quantum physics or QED (quantum electro-dynamics).

As we have seen, radionic therapy includes not only an assessment, or analysis, but also treatment of a patient's illness at a distance (or 'projection', as it is sometimes called). This part of the procedure is not subject to the normal limits of space and time; a practitioner in England can give distant treatment to a sleeping patient in Australia, for example.

Professional practitioners are trained in the use of radionic instruments for both analysis and treatment. However, before a student practitioner obtains their certificate of competency, he or she normally undergoes additional training in biology and anatomy. There are many doctors and other healthcare professionals who use radionics as a diagnostic tool because it can detect many underlying causes of illness that are often missed by some of the more conventional procedures.

In the days of Abrams, all those years ago, both the analysis and treatment instruments were black-painted wooden boxes containing various electronic components. Today's radionics instruments, though smaller and more refined in appearance, use magnetism, electricity, sound or light waves to function and are still all made of wood or black plastic. Thus the radionic 'black boxes' continue to play a vital role in the healing of illness.

In this new millennium we are seeing a renaissance in mind–body medicine, a revival of many traditional alternative therapies that offer a spiritual dimension as well as a path to physical health and wellbeing. Like some of these other therapies, radionics provides patients with a reason for their ailments, sometimes of a subtle or even esoteric nature. With the help of a well-trained practitioner, they receive comfort and encouragement to participate and have faith in the treatment being provided.

Patients today are more perceptive, and want to know more about the healthcare they receive. They want to know why a condition exists and they want to use therapies that will not hinder their recovery or produce insidious side-effects. This is where radionics has an advantage over conventional therapies using chemicals to alter physical body conditions. Because the radionic treatment acts at a subtle level, it allows the innate intelligence within the body to enact the healing, with no unwanted side-effects. In a sense, radionics reminds the body of how it *should* be functioning.

Radionics has its critics, not surprisingly. Some argue that it's all in the mind of the patient. As with homeopathy, others say that if a dose of a remedy contains no traceable amount of the original substance used in its preparation it must mean it's having a placebo effect. Observing a radionic practitioner at work, there are no visible signs that measurable energy is emanating from the sample taken from a patient, other than its effect upon the practitioner's instruments. Likewise, the radionic projections emanating from the treatment instrument cannot be felt, heard or seen when in the practitioner's consulting room.

In this brief guide I hope to present enough argument and evidence to give the critics of radionics and homeopathy pause for thought. Then they may be able to stand back and take another view of energy medicine in general.

About this book

This book gives guidance on how to find a radionic practitioner and what to expect when you do find one. It explains how you will be expected to complete a brief case history and examples are given of a typical case history sheet and the type of information your practitioner will require. There are also examples of radionic reports given to patients. All patients should request these, as the written word is so useful to refer to when you are sick; it gives confidence and helps affirm the healing thoughts required.

The book also contains some amazing examples of human, animal and plant treatments. Because radionics deals with the formative energies of electromagnetic fields (see Chapter 3), it is capable of treating all living organisms. These fields of force create the actual matter we see before our eyes. By studying the subtle formative energy around a body, a radionic practitioner can spot a general lack of wellbeing *before* a named illness is diagnosed and really takes hold. Chapter 1 describes how the manufacture of radionic remedies for oral use takes place. These are not only homeopathic remedies but also other substances that can be used for treating allergies.

Numerous, often amusing case studies are given with typical comments from long-standing patients, such as, 'Hello, I'm in Australia and I've got a tummy bug. Please put me on the black box.' Meanwhile, in her radionic animal practice, my wife gets regular requests such as, 'Please put *Visor* on the black box. His feet are killing him again. It worked wonders last month, he came first in his class.'

So, is radionics 'all in the mind'? I believe that both the analytical and treatment procedures actually take place in the minds of the practitioner and patient, and they also affect the patient's body. By learning more about these procedures in radionics we can start to understand why they work on humans, animals and plants. This guide to radionics is based on my own personal views and the knowledge I have accumulated from thirty years of practical radionic experience. I hope it will bring about a lateral shift in the way we think about ourselves and the world around us.

Chapter 1

Defining Radionics

THE WORD RADIONICS is derived from the two words 'radiation' and 'electronics' (the measurement and use of radiation electronically). The term was first coined in the early twentieth century. This chapter provides an introductory summary of radionics; most of the aspects covered receive more detailed explanation later in the book.

Radionics is often defined as 'holistic distant healing', a form of vibrational medicine that can discover the energy imbalances in a patient. The practitioner then 'broadcasts' or projects corrective energy patterns back to the patient via the hair sample (which is placed upon specialised radionic instruments).

The radiesthetic or extra-sensory perception faculty (known as ESP), used in radionics, is sensitive to the subtle vibrations emanating from the energy fields of the patient and their hair sample, often referred to as the 'patient's witness'. All living organisms and naturally occurring medicines also emit a detectable energy field.

During the initial analysis or assessment of the patient's symptoms the practitioner looks at the individual energy patterns of known physical body structures in the patient. In addition the practitioner will search for irregularities in both the mental and emotional regions. These unseen yet profoundly important mental and emotional activity areas can be measured in the individual chakras or energy centres (which correspond to the physical glandular systems of the body).

Chakras or energy centres exist near the major glands in the human and animal body. They are detectable through ESP and electrically sensitive cameras. Literally translated, the word chakra means 'wheel'. Chakras are vortices of energy, as described by Tibetan and Indian philosophers. They contain both the positive and negative electromagnetic energy that gives the corresponding glands and organs in the physical body the ability to attain wellbeing or develop illness. Within these energy centres or chakras are the force fields that control both input and output of the positive and negative thought forms that make up our varying personalities.

Measurements are made on radionic assessment instruments by comparing the status of the hair sample with the patterns of energy set up on the radionic analysis instrument. The assessment is carried out by means of questions.

The responses to the questions posed in the practitioner's mind, such as, 'What is the degree of deviation from functional perfection of the pituitary gland of this patient, Mrs Smith?', are monitored within the practitioner's own nervous system by the swing of the pendulum. This pendulum information is then transformed into conscious data by the neurone activity of the brain. The neurone activity influences the pendulum response over the radionic instrument upon which the patient's hair sample is placed. The responses are recorded on datasheets.

According to radionic philosophy, the physical human body is governed by minute atomic structures that make up energy fields. These energy fields surround each individual cell and the whole human body itself, including the mental and emotional fields.

The latest treatment method used to transfer corrective energy to the patient is *thought*. This happens instantly, transcending both space and time, via specialised radionic instruments powered by light photons.

Radionic treatment can be used with conventional and alternative therapies alike, as it acts in a complementary manner. And it has the added advantage that the patient's presence is not needed for treatment. A snippet of the patient's hair (the witness) acts as the link between patient and radionic practitioner during the analysis and treatment procedures.

Radionics assists the patient's innate self-healing ability, because it facilitates the flow of energy between the physical body and the mind. This includes both the emotional and mental activities, often referred to as the subtle bodies.

Alongside the physical DNA, there appears to be a parallel or subtle DNA (effectively a blueprint of every person's life). This pattern of energy is in every cell of our bodies, including our hair, and each cell reflects the total energy pattern of the whole person.

The hair sample maintains a 'resonant link' with the source (the patient) at all times. To understand this concept think of cellular biology, in which each cell carries a copy of the master plan (or blueprint) of the whole, the DNA.

From the data obtained through a radionic assessment, an individual blueprint of the patient's total health is built up. This will include the underlying causes of the symptoms the patient displays physically, mentally or emotion-ally. Because radionic analysis and assessment unravels these underlying causes of illnesses, it is possible to discover and treat them in their very early stages – before the symptoms become apparent. Patients who complain of feeling generally unwell can be treated straight away, by correcting energy imbalances in the energy patterns of their subtle body areas.

A miasm is often referred to as an energy imbalance that predisposes a person to develop certain illnesses or disease patterns similar to those experienced by our forefathers. Those people with deeper spiritual beliefs consider miasms to be brought forward from previous incarnations and illnesses experienced during that lifetime.

Treatment rates are given to patients by placing the witness (or hair sample) in the radionic treatment instrument. The corrective energy patterns are supplied via coded numerical sequences on dials (rates), or by insertion of cards carrying geometric patterns. (For more on these cards, see page 34.)

Radionic analysis and instruments can be powered by electricity, magnetism or light. All are equally effective at transferring healing thoughts.

The corrective energy patterns used for the patients can be varied. They may take the form of functional patterns for physical organs or subtle bodies; or energy patterns of elements, tissue salts, minerals or vitamins.

The treatment projections can include other energetic vibrations, such as Dr Bach Flower Remedies, colour, homeopathic remedies, and corrective patterns for psychological states along with antidote patterns for viruses and allergies.

All of the above energy patterns may be simulated (or prepared) in radionic instruments as personal remedies for oral use by treating directly in the instrument some medicated water or sac lac (milk sugar tablets) and then administering to the patient.

In conclusion, there are no limits to what radionic treatment can be used for. Successful treatment can be given for acute and chronic physical illnesses, mental and emotional illness, as well as psychological states and hypersensitivity. Radionics complements both orthodox human and veterinary medicine.

Illnesses that respond well to radionic treatment include asthma and allergies such as hay fever; migraines and headaches; female disorders such as heavy periods and pre-menstrual tension; muscular and skeletal conditions including arthritic symptoms; digestive disturbances and bowel problems. Mental illness and hypersensitivity, along with psychological symptoms, respond well to radionics, as does cancer (as the therapy acts in a complementary manner to help the patient deal with chemotherapy and radiation). Radionics is known to assist the body in self-healing and is particularly useful following surgery.

Chapter 2

The History
of Radionics

THE ACTUAL BIRTHPLACE of radionics was San Francisco. The founding father, Dr Albert Abrams, was born in 1863 into a wealthy merchant family but he decided to follow a career in medicine rather than in the world of commerce. As a young man, he studied German, attended the University of Heidelberg in Germany, and graduated with an M.D. and an M.A. He returned to the USA and became Professor of Pathology and ultimately Director of Clinical Medicine at Leland Stanford University. He was a fellow of the American Medical Association and acquired a national reputation as an expert on diseases of the nervous system. Dr Abrams was a workaholic, using his inherited wealth to further contemporary medical research, and writing a total of twelve books.

He was highly acclaimed by his peers until one fateful day, when he accidentally made an interesting discovery that would eventually lead to him being violently condemned by the very same medical and scientific community. During an examination of a patient suffering a malignant ulcer on the lip, Abrams was routinely tapping the abdomen. To his surprise, he found the palpation caused a dull and heavy-sounding note instead of the usual hollow sound. Abrams palpated the abdomen further to find out whether any mass or other physical abnormality was responsible for the dull sound, but found nothing.

Continuing his examination, he discovered that the same sound could be detected time after time when the patient faced a particular direction. The significance of his discovery was reinforced by the fact that this particular sound from the abdomen was the same on all the patients he tested who were suffering from cancer. He brought in healthy patients, orientating them in similar directions, and found only the normal hollow sound when palpating the abdomen; whereas, without exception, all cancer patients – when facing in a particular direction – emitted the same dull abdominal sound.

Abrams then gave the healthy subject a phial to hold containing malignant tissue and again he obtained the dull heavy sound. He took away the phial of diseased tissue – hollow sound. He replaced the phial in the subject's hand – dull sound. The experiment highlighted two phenomena as far as Abrams was concerned. Firstly, he believed it showed that disease was not so much a matter of cellular imbalance as an imbalance of the electrons of the atoms of the diseased tissue or body. Disease appeared to be a form of radiating energy, detectable by Abrams' palpation techniques. Secondly, the radiating energy emitted by the diseased material travelled through the body of a healthy individual and could be measured.

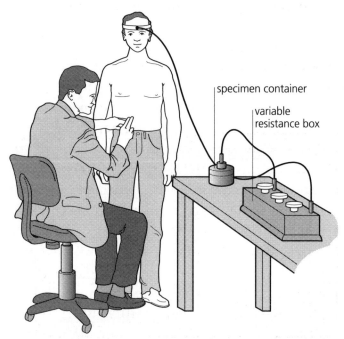

specimen container

variable resistance box

Figure 1 Illustration showing diagnostic apparatus similar to that used by Dr Abrams when palpating the abdomen of a healthy male subject.

He also found that radiation from diseased tissue could be transmitted down a wire. (Subjects would hold a wire connected to the phial and the same note would be detected when their abdomens were palpated.) This reaction was known at the time as ERA (the Electronic Reaction of Abrams) and was, in effect, the beginning of what is now known as radionics. The word radionics is derived from the two words 'radiation' and 'electronics'. This is really what the therapy is all about, the measurement and use of radiation electronically.

To return to Abrams and his work in the early twentieth century, he also found that the abdominal sounds emitted by cancer patients differed from those suffering tuberculosis and again from those who had syphilis.

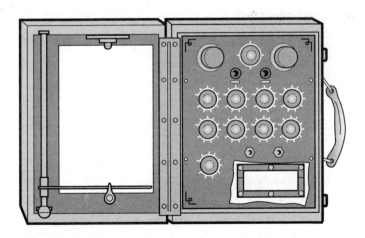

Figure 2 Example of an early portable radionic analysis and treatment instrument about the size of a small suitcase.

As it had already been proven years before that radiation could travel down wires, Abrams created a variable resistance box (see Figure 1) to measure it. Using this instrument, he found that cancerous tissue measured 50 ohms, while a syphilitic tissue sample measured 55 ohms. These experiments led to the listing of resistance settings for known diseases. All the measurements were eventually gathered together in a book of resistance rates. This has been considerably expanded and rewritten many times by new generations of researchers, but they are still known and used today as 'radionic rates' with set numerical values. We now have numerical rates (see Figure 3) for all the physical and subtle body areas and for named diseases. These are used when assessing patients. In addition there are comparable treatment rates for radionic projection and treatment instruments. These rates and systems form the basis of radionics, all of which must be ascribed to Abrams.

RADIONICS ARRIVES IN GREAT BRITAIN

As communication and travel improved in the 1920s, news of Abrams' work duly arrived in England, and there was increased pressure upon the British medical establishment to examine the claims made by Abrams' supporters in the USA.

Conditions		*Joints*	
Impinged nerves	90.63	Wrist	84910041
Strain	60.93865	Shoulder	8493323
Sciatica	40.351935	Mandible	8491736
Lumbago	40.599193	Sacro-iliac	849923
Trauma	10.92		
Fractured ribs	90. 7542	*Minerals*	
		Radium	834300
Bones		Lead	8341609
Elbow	84115	Iodine	834884
Ankle	841893	Carbon	83487
Fingers	84895	Iron	834492
Pelvis	84525		
Knee	84121	*Remedies*	
Right hip	84479	Aconitum	901558
Left hip	84439	Belladonna	901448
		Conium	9015239
Vertebrae			
Cervical	84692	*Gases*	
Dorsal	84183	Chlorine	6789301
Coccyx	84188	Hydrogen	6789169
Sacral	84854	Oxygen	6789263

Figure 3 Examples of typical radionic rates, some of which were devised by Ruth Drown, that are used on the dial type radionic analysis and treatment instruments.

A team of investigators was set up, under the supervision of Sir Thomas Horder (who later became Lord Horder). Twenty-five tests were carried out (in London in May 1924 and in Glasgow in June of the same year) at radionic researcher, Dr Boyd's laboratory in the presence of an eminent physicist named Mr Whately Smith. Using an instrument called a Boyd's Emanometer, which detected the ERA reaction, they attempted to distinguish between phials containing homeopathic sulphur and others containing similar amounts of neutral material.

The committee and its overseer Lord Horder were amazed to find that, in every test, every phial had been correctly identified (without the instrument's operator having any opportunity to see the contents of the phial or influence the result). The effectiveness of Abrams' method of detecting electromagnetic fields had now been firmly established within the British medical establishment. Or had it?

BACK TO THE USA

On the contrary, the medical establishment of the time refused to endorse the work of Abrams and collectively turned their backs on radionics, hoping it would go away (at least from British shores). And this is exactly what happened. But the radionic torch, though temporarily dimmed, flickered into life again, this time back where it had originated in the USA. The flame was re-kindled in the 1930s by a chiropractor called Dr Ruth Drown who was practising in Hollywood, California. She developed the Electronic Reaction of Abrams instrument still further by replacing the human subject in the circuit with a sample of their blood or hair. This blood or hair sample was placed in a metal phial with the circuit wires attached.

The known rates for a disease (see page 25) were then dialled up and set on the instrument.

To assess the reaction, Ruth Drown invented a measuring device in the form of a rubber diaphragm covering a metal detector plate in the circuit. If the response was positive, she obtained a 'sticking' sensation when she rubbed her fingers over the rubber. If the disease was not present in the patient, there was no reaction.

The diagnosis of the patient's ills happened normally with the patient present in her practice rooms, but when treatment was given for the disease detected the patient was 'hooked' into the circuit just as Abrams had done for both diagnosis and treatment. Dr Drown argued that, if we all live in the vast electromagnetic energy field that surrounds this planet, it is surely reasonable to assume that we are all affected by this field. Using this assumption, Ruth Drown was the first person to circulate the patient's own energetic life force through the instrument and then to modify it by the resistance rates set up on the instrument dials to cure the disease.

RADIONIC TREATMENT AT A DISTANCE

Thinking more deeply about the earth's energy fields, Ruth Drown made another assumption that led her to conduct a further experiment. This time she took the patient out of the treatment circuit (as well as the assessment circuit) and replaced the patient with his or her blood sample.

She then set up the rates for the particular disease and allowed the earth's energy fields to treat the patient at a distance. This she called 'broadcasting'; it is more commonly known as 'radionic projections' today. Dr Drown could now diagnose and treat a patient at a distance using the patient's blood sample as a witness. The patient could be anywhere – across town, or in another country – and she still obtained the same results.

To the average person at the time this must have sounded very far-fetched, and it probably still sounds pretty outlandish to many people. Here was a doctor of chiropractic medicine, well-qualified and respected by her patients, diagnosing their ailments without seeing them and making them well by treating their blood samples. Furthermore, she continued her research and eventually developed a camera attached to the radionic instrument that enabled her to take photographs, via the blood sample, of the inside of the patient. This was tantamount to throwing X-ray equipment out of the window. How was all this possible?

The patient could be anywhere in the world, complain of a stomach disorder, and contact Dr Drown. She would have the patient's sample and take a picture of the stomach on the photographic plate attached to the instrument. She would then develop this photograph to diagnose what was wrong, and treat the patient for the condition she had diagnosed.

THE BRITISH PIONEERS

Not surprisingly, this amazing lady was pursued by the medical establishment and the food and drug administration of the State of California. She was accused of fraud, on the grounds that her instruments were non-scientific and did not achieve the results she claimed. The continual harassment and defamation affected Ruth Drown's health and sadly she died in 1966, a martyr to the cause of radionics.

Over the last twenty years I have spent some time in the company of one of England's most eminent radionic practitioners, Mrs Lavender Dower, who in turn knew Dr Ruth Drown in the 1960s. Lavender has told me about some interesting aspects of Ruth Drown's work, as well as the work of other pioneers in radionics. On the subject of radionic instruments, I remember Lavender once saying: 'If we had learned to use the full potential of our minds, radionic instruments would not be necessary. But, alas, we have as yet only learned to use one-tenth of our brain, and the strain of holding a thought in absolute clarity and providing the energy to project it to the patient would strictly limit our usefulness. With the aid of radionic instruments we can help many more people than would be possible without them.'

Lavender Dower met many important researchers in her lifetime. One of these was

George De La Warr, an engineer who left his post as chief engineering assistant to Oxfordshire County Council to devote himself to the continuing research and treatment of patients by radionics. As well as De La Warr, there was a Dr W. Guyon Richards who in 1954 completed an epic book called *The Chain of Life*. This lucidly explained the fundamental principles and theories, as well as the technical details, of radiesthesia and radionics from the early Abrams experiments right up to the 1950s. Many distinguished doctors began using radionics and by the end of the 1960s the radionic torch was well alight and burning brightly. Radionics was back in Britain, with a professional medical following as well as many lay practitioners.

In the UK George De La Warr developed a similar camera to Ruth Drown which he used to take over 12,000 photographs of energy fields that emanated from various objects. Three photographs appear in David Tansley's book called *Radionics: A Patient's Guide* (see Further Reading). One photograph shows a three-month-old foetus. Because the formative energy contained in one cell (subtle DNA) is contained in all the cells of the body, the blood sample from a pregnant woman was placed on the witness plate of the radionic camera. The numerical rate for a three-month-old foetus was set up on the camera and a film slid into the light-tight box and left for 15 seconds. The film was then withdrawn, developed and printed. The image obtained showed clearly the three-month-old foetus existing in the womb. Yet the woman concerned was fifty miles away from the camera when her blood sample was photographed.

According to Tansley, a doctor actually took one of these radionic cameras into a teaching hospital for research and was threatened with dismissal by his superiors.

In the late 1960s David Tansley, a chiropractor who had trained in the USA, came to Britain. He had an immediate impact on the radionic scene. He joined the Radionic Association in 1967, after being introduced to the therapy by Dr Aubrey Westlake (another pioneer of complementary and radionic medicine). David quite rightly observed that, at the time, radionic teaching and all its instrumentation and analytical techniques were slanted towards the use of medical models of anatomy and pathology (perhaps in order to gain acceptance by the orthodox medical system). However, David realised that radionics was actually a highly effective form of energy medicine. Forcing it to conform to a physical medical model imposed severe limitations on its power.

David Tansley liked to speak his mind, and he put the proverbial cat amongst the pigeons in the late 1960s by introducing eastern philosophy to western-style radionics. For many practitioners, myself included, this was a major turning

point, introducing a new philosophical dimension. Eastern philosophy already accepted the
esoteric (or energetic) origins of humankind and
had mapped out the unseen aspects of the human
form. According to many eastern systems of
medicine, mental attitudes, emotional factors and
other environmental energies could influence
health as well as being causative factors in illness.
Radionics no longer had to rely solely upon
observable symptoms and the medical diagnosis
of the physical; it could now identify the mental
and emotional causes of illness as well.

David Tansley's book *Subtle Anatomy of
Man* (published in 1972) proved beyond doubt
the existence of detectable and recordable energy
fields surrounding the human form, the
endocrine glands and organ systems, and became
a core text for students of radionics. David introduced the concept of measuring the activity of the
energy vortices (known as 'chakras' in India and
Tibet). He also demonstrated that illness and
disease appeared to manifest in these subtle areas
before causing pathological symptoms in the
physical body. Between 1972 and the mid-1980s
David produced many books outlining his
research, aimed at both medical doctors and
lay practitioners. Radionics in the 1980s was
flourishing, but change was on the way.

THE LAST TWENTY YEARS OF RADIONICS

Overlooking the Avon valley in Hampshire is a small village called Godshill. In the early 1980s this village was the hub of radionics in England – if not the world.

David Tansley and I lived on the woodland estate owned by Dr Aubrey Westlake at Godshill and all three of us practised and researched this extraordinary therapy. For many years doctors and researchers in radionics and energy medicine visited us from all over the world, learning the techniques we had developed. Eventually David moved to Australia for a period of time. But after returning to England, to the saddened astonishment of all radionic followers, he died very suddenly. To add to this loss, Dr Westlake also passed away, very peacefully and well into his ninety-second year.

My wife and I remained at Godshill working closely with the London-based company Magneto Geometric Applications, founded by the late Malcolm Rae. I had been in regular contact with Malcolm Rae during the 1970s, whilst I still lived in South Africa, and had successfully used his newly developed radionic instruments.

It was the combined gifts of these three eminent researchers – David Tansley's esoteric philosophy, the perceptive rationalism of

Malcolm Rae, and Dr Westlake's steadfast medical wisdom – that enabled radionics to make a quantum leap into a new and exciting era. This era began in the last fifteen years of the twentieth century.

From the time of Abrams and Drown through to De La Warr, radionic instruments were powered by electricity. (All instruments need a power source in order to operate, and allow measurements to be taken and recorded.) It was Malcolm Rae who first used magnetism instead of electricity. In so doing he was able to make radionic instruments easily portable. Even more enticing, the new magnetic instruments could simulate (or mimic) the energetic values of homeopathic remedies for oral use. In addition Malcolm Rae moved away from the time-consuming twiddling of numerous dials for each radionic operation to simply dropping a reference card in a slot.

These reference or simulator cards are rectangular in shape with an inscribed circle containing measured radii representing the pattern of the organ or structure being treated (see Figure 4). The radionic analysing instruments are then used to measure how far the structure or organ deviates from normality or to reveal any illness that may be present. Using the cards, a radionic analysis that had previously taken two or three hours could be carried out in a matter of minutes.

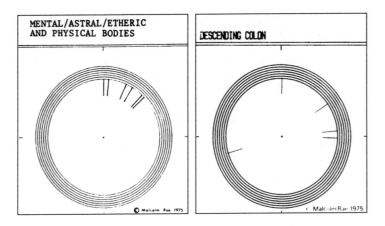

Figure 4 Typical Malcolm Rae cards – one for subtle bodies and the other for a particular body part (descending colon).

In the last few years an additional medium for powering radionic instruments has emerged. This medium is light (and its inherent photons or biophotons, as they are referred to in radionic practice), a form of energy studied by quantum physicists. Conceived by eminent physicians, drawing on the doctrines of ancient philosophy, and now successfully complementing proven alternative and conventional therapies, radionics can today take its place as a fully fledged energy medicine.

Using the principles of quantum physics, radionics endeavours to energise and heal the subtle, unseen dimensions of the human body. Illness appears to manifest in the concealed dimensions of the human form before developing pathological, recognisable symptoms. Perhaps, orthodox medicine should therefore direct its research efforts to this subtle realm, to establish exactly what causes atoms and elements (the building blocks of the universe) to construct, and destroy, living form. Radionic practitioners are already using the principles of quantum electro-dynamics (or QED) in their daily assessment and treatment of patients' illnesses, as we will discover in the next chapter.

Chapter 3

The Subtle Workings of 21st-Century Radionics

I T IS WITHIN THE microscopic workings of the human body that twenty-first-century radionics has its influence. This is why radionics is so effective in manipulating the minute electromagnetic energy fields that cause both wellbeing and illness in the living form, whether vegetable, animal or human.

Unlike radionics, conventional medicine bases its theory and treatment procedures on two main philosophies, biology and chemistry. However, the most important philosophy, which controls the functioning of all living matter including the human body, is physics and particularly quantum physics. Modern radionic schools spend considerable time teaching students the principles of quantum physics and how this discipline relates to radionic assessment and treatment procedures. There is only space here for a brief introduction to the subject. For a more detailed account of the elemental make-up of the human body, readers may wish to refer to my recently published book *Thoughts that Harm, Thoughts that Heal*.

ELECTROMAGNETIC FIELDS

Scientists accept that the atoms of all matter are held together by minute electromagnetic force (a theory known as quantum electrodynamics or QED). This is the primary sphere in which radionics operates. And, as this book unfolds, I will frequently refer to the electromagnetic fields that control the energy centres (or vortices), glands and organ systems of the body.

Imagine a choreographed electron dance, in which electrically charged particles orbit a central nucleus and interact with other electrons orbiting other nuclei; this is sometimes called an electromagnetic field. It's like a minuscule version of our solar system, where all the planets continually orbit the sun. This dance of atoms and electrons goes on inside each and every cell of the human body. In a similar way, much larger fields of energy surround the whole body. So we have minute energy fields in every cell of our bodies which are, in turn, surrounded by larger fields of energy. These energy fields contain the blueprint or matrix of the cell structures, as well as the person's mental and emotional state, personality and general constitution.

As we know, the atoms and molecules of which we are composed all contain electrons moving in orbit about a central nucleus. This is the foundation of the stable elemental complexes and compounds (combinations of various elements) that make up the cells and the body as a whole.

All life is based upon chemical elements. These include the solid, liquid and gas elements of which our physical bodies are constructed and upon which we rely for nutrition. We have all heard of mineral elements like calcium, magnesium, zinc and selenium. Many people regularly take these as dietary supplements. So it's really all elementary. The elements make up the chemistry and the chemistry makes up the organs, tissues and bones of the human form. If we are to take more responsibility for our own health, it is important to know a little about the make-up of our bodies and about the role the elements and minerals play in nourishing us and keeping us in a state of wellbeing. The atomic structures of nature (protons and electrons) form the basis of the elements, and the elements go on to form the enzymes and proteins that make up the body.

Modern research, carried out worldwide on animals, humans and plants, published by Milner and Smart in their book *Loom of Creation* (see Further Reading), has confirmed the existence of electromagnetic energy around all cellular structures within the living form. Equally, electromagnetic fields have been shown to exist around the natural supplements used to treat human and animal illnesses, most dramatically in energy field photographs and homeopathic remedies and their changing dilution (see Figure 5). This phenomenon does not exist in crude laboratory-produced drugs or in processed foods.

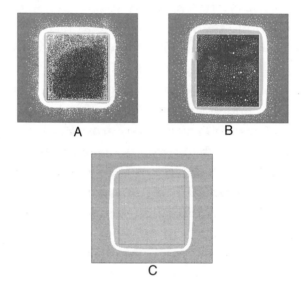

Figure 5 Three examples of electro-magnetic field photographs from the work of Milner and Smart. A is a homeopathic dilution of pulsatilla, B and C are further dilutions showing a change from darker to lighter shades as the potency increases and the electro-magnetic field intensifies.

In recent times there has been considerable discussion about the human mind and medicine, and the power attributed to the mind as it influences the body. A number of successful cancer treatment techniques have been based purely upon visualisation and the focusing of the mind. It is of course impossible to observe these methods in progress; one can only witness the results. The explanation for their success is that the person must be tapping into the unseen electrical force fields surrounding their mind and its thought processes as well as the physical structure itself. Likewise, when a healer is performing a therapeutic treatment on a patient, it is possible to reorganise the energies surrounding the cells and the body structures, creating order from chaos.

Energy fields can be disturbed for a number of reasons, including invading viruses, physical and mechanical injuries, suppressed emotions, and lack of communication. Energy medicine (radionics) uses delicate instruments to measure the vibrations emanating from a single cell. This provides information about imbalances within the cellular structures, and the radionic practitioner's interpretation of this information identifies the possible causes of the patient's symptoms. It also provides the information needed for correct remedy selection, which can again be verified using the radionic instrument.

Historically, the great radionic practitioners of the last century used another tool – extrasensory perception (or ESP) – in their analysis and treatment of patients. Modern radionic students still learn the principles of ESP and the use of a pendulum, but the main vehicle for radionic influence nowadays is thought.

Thought is in fact an electromagnetic field that can affect other electromagnetic fields. This is why radionic assessment can gather information about a patient on the other side of the earth. To gain this information the practitioner requires a sample or witness from the patient and the most common, and least painful to obtain, is a piece of hair. There are some radionic practitioners who use a blood spot or saliva sample, but hair is the most convenient medium.

THE SAMPLE OR WITNESS

One of the hardest concepts for people to grasp is the special connection of the hair sample, once removed, to the patient's current state of health. There are three major questions that we radionic practitioners regularly hear, even from long-standing patients who have experienced the effectiveness of radionic assessment and treatment for themselves. These questions include:

- What's in the hair sample that allows you to analyse and prescribe remedies for my illness?

- What happens if the hair is dyed?

- Why don't you need a new hair sample each time you work on me?

- And how can you possibly treat me when I am many miles away from your office?

To answer these and other questions, let's start by looking at what normally happens in a radionic consultation and course of treatment.

Patients submit a sample of hair, normally in a small envelope. A few strands of hair can be cut from the head hair and placed between two sticky labels, with the patient's name written on one side. This sample acts as a witness, symbolising the patient's request for treatment. The patient also completes and returns a case history questionnaire. (This questionnaire will be discussed in detail in Chapter 5.)

The most important aspect of the sample is that it provides what we call in radionics 'a subtle DNA' (or blueprint) of that patient's life. The radionic practitioner uses the hair sample to make a connection for information to flow on the 'thoughtstring' (or link) between the mind of the practitioner and the mind of the patient. This process exists whether analysing humans or animals, as the patient's subconscious or creative mind is aware of all that is manifesting in the patient's body.

Although cut hair is often considered to be dead material it is in fact very much alive. Its rate of decay is minimal, showing that its atomic structure must be fairly stable. Hair is often found on bodies mummified thousands of years ago. And I have hair samples from patients submitted to me for analysis some thirty years ago, from which I can complete assessments on their present state of health if requested. This last statement probably raises one of those common questions in your mind: how can an old sample relate to a patient's current health status? This is the most profound and interesting part of radionic philosophy that enables practitioners to glean information from the sample for assessment of health and in turn can use the sample to transmit healing energies to the patient irrespective of the age of the sample used. The fact is that time and distance play no part in radionics and this is one of the main stumbling blocks that prevents more patients from registering with a practitioner: the whole concept of treatment at a distance is too perplexing for many people.

In the radionic procedure there has to be a direct link between the practitioner and the patient. The patient has to *intentionally* allow the practitioner to gather the information. One of the few exceptions to this rule is surrogate consultations (for instance, when a mother asks for help for her child or a relative seeks help, with permission from a family member or friend). The other exception is when an animal owner submits the sick animal's sample for analysis; the connection is still present in the form of the animal's hair sample, the animal owner and the practitioner, and a triangular link is made.

This link, thought connection, or thought-string, transcends time and distance, and thus lies within the realm of quantum theory. To understand what this means, we need to learn a little more about the work of particle physicists – work which has overturned many of our assumptions about the nature of reality.

THE EPR EXPERIMENT

According to Albert Einstein, no signal or influence could travel faster than the speed of light. He denied that electrons could influence each other's motion and position, even a few metres apart let alone light-years apart, and called it 'ghostly action at a distance'.

However, the EPR experiment (so-called after the eminent physicists Einstein, Podolsky and Rosen, who first conducted it in the 1930s) disproved Einstein's theory, providing a good example of a situation in which a quantum phenomenon clashes with our traditional understanding of reality.

The experiment involves two balanced spinning electrons, both sharing the same angle of axis but spinning in different directions. (These electrons have to be taken from a balanced atomic structure, such as a hair sample.) In the EPR physics experiment they are then separated from one another by a huge distance. Let's say 'particle one' is in New York and 'particle two' is in Los Angeles or even on the other side of the world. This enormous separation does not interfere with their spin or axis. But the instant an observer of 'particle one' makes a measurement or change of spin or axis, 'particle two' will change its axis or spin accordingly in a re-balancing act.

There is no time for 'particle two' to receive information about the change by any conventional signal. A measurement performed on one particle has an instant effect on the other far-distant particle. Einstein called this 'ghostly action at a distance'.

The principle underlying Einstein's theory of relativity, that nothing travels faster than the speed of light, had been demolished. The action-at-a-distance experiment proved that thought (that is, *thinking about taking action*, which actually causes action at a distance) does travel faster than the speed of light; thought is in fact instantaneous.

Thought affects the actions of electrons, which affect the performance of the atoms they govern, which then affect the performance of the elements which make up all living matter. This is how positive or negative thought can produce wellbeing or its reverse, ill-health. However, people need to understand that exterior negative thoughts can only be received if the recipient is open to accepting them. This is why it is so important for patients and practitioners to understand the importance of expressing the request for healing and the intention to receive it.

Radionics now has a proven theory, endorsed by eminent physicists, that action at a distance takes place through the power of thought. The hair sample sent in by the patient and used by the practitioner is similar to 'particle one' in the EPR experiment. The body of the patient (from whom the sample was cut) represents 'particle two'. The distance between the sample and the patient at any one time is immaterial and irrelevant to any procedure the radionic practitioner wishes to conduct.

The practitioner places the patient's hair sample upon a special radionic instrument and poses mental questions (as described in Chapter 1) about the status of the patient's health. The radionic analysis procedure is similar to an EPR experiment, in that each time the practitioner poses a question in their mind, information passes between sample and patient (just as it passes between 'particle one' and 'particle two'). The thought transference is instantaneous and this is what makes radionics possible. Figure 6 shows the triangular link between sample, patient and practitioner's mind, and how information flows in both directions simultaneously.

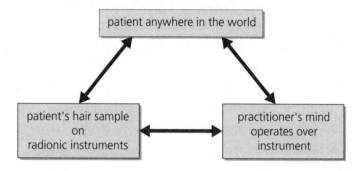

Figure 6 The triangulation of thought used in radionics and distant healing.

THOUGHTSTRING OR SUPER-STRING?

To a radionic practitioner, who assesses the cause of many patients' symptoms from hair samples and subsequently treats those patients at a distance in their daily practice, the 'action at a distance' (still vehemently debated in scientific circles) is an everyday phenomenon. For those patients who are successfully treated, the reasons why it works are unimportant. The main point is that they have regained their health. Many readers of this guide may also be willing to simply accept that healing occurs. But, for others who wish to know more about the scientific theories behind the radionic practice of distant healing, here is a brief discussion of more recent developments in quantum physics and their relevance to radionics.

During the 1990s, physicists made fascinating discoveries about the behaviour of particles like electrons and quarks. They found that these particles, which hold the atomic world in a basically stable yet dynamic state, are composed of even smaller entities called 'strings'. As their name suggests, these new entities differ from the familiar multicoloured billiard-ball diagrams we have all seen in books explaining how matter inter-links with itself and builds the living structures in our world. These newly discovered particles can literally extend like a piece of string.

The EPR experiment proved that there was an instant correlation between separated particles over enormous distances. Some physicists now believe that this instant correlation may be established through the new third particle: the super-string. For the last twenty years, many of the theories within quantum physics have appeared to run completely counter to common sense. They still do, but physicists now believe it may be possible to pull together quantum theory and relativity theory into one coherent string theory. How long this will take no one knows.

Even though I am definitely a layman when it comes to quantum physics, I am convinced – due to my experiences of healing at a distance – that the third particle or super-string the physicists speak of is closely related to what I call a 'thoughtstring'. Just as we string together thoughts within our minds, it must be possible to project these thoughts anywhere in the universe, unconstrained by space or time.

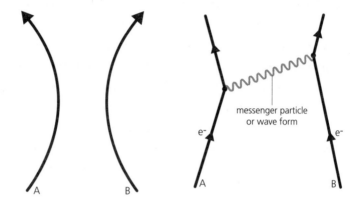

Figure 7 In the left-hand illustration, particle A avoids or repels particle B, whereas in the example on the right the messenger particle provides the correct information to attract or repel the particles ('thoughtstring' theory).

According to the physicists' super-string theory, the building blocks of the universe (that is the protons, neutrons and electrons) are not elementary particles, as had long been thought, but rather tiny massless strings that vibrate at a specific frequency and twist or rotate in space (see Figure 7). This theory finds an echo in traditional Chinese medicine's theory of energy as 'chi' which passes through unseen meridian channels or pathways in the body. These subtle pathways or meridians cannot be traced or identified by conventional scans. Similarly, radionics, as well as other energy medicine systems, assumes the existence of energy centres and pathways of energy surrounding the physical form. A body of scientific knowledge exists that considers that thought precedes all action. The matterless energy of the electromagnetic fields is of a quantum nature, and must surround all living matter and indeed precedes the formation of all living substance. Is it not then plausible to suggest that thought is actually a vibration that becomes a resonance, similar to that of the electromagnetic energy fields existing around matter? This can be compared with the known duality existing in the wave/form particle theory of quantum physics that scientists use to explain the creation of living matter. These fields of energy can be seen in Kirlian photographs, which show the actual energy emanating from nature's structures.

The super-string theory expounded by physicists (my thoughtstring) connects the two particles via the mind of the practitioner when conducting the EPR experiment, this being the instant action at a distance. The information relayed from one particle to the other beyond the speed of light can in my opinion only be via thought: a thoughtstring of the mind.

Interestingly, humankind spends vast quantities of energy and money researching the origins of matter, and almost nothing investigating the origins of mind and thought. Yet mind and matter are inextricably linked. Mind appears to hold the memory, as well as the knowledge, of all that goes on within the body physically, mentally and emotionally. And thought is the vehicle by which that information is transferred.

During my years in radionic practice many people have intimated that, had I lived a few centuries ago and practised the work I do now, I would have been locked away – if not put to death. However, a reference in the works of the Elizabethan philosopher Francis Bacon written as long ago as 1672, implies that distant healing is not nearly as new as people might think. Bacon wrote, 'It is constantly received and avouched, that the anointing of the weapon that maketh the wound, will heal the wound itself.' He then described the preparation of an ointment, and the various tests to which the practice had been subjected. All the tests seemed to show that the cure was obtained only when the ointment was applied to the weapon and not the wound, and though the weapon might be a great distance away, the cure did not depend upon the patient knowing of the anointing.

The probable explanation is that the victim's blood, or witness, remained on the sword. The anointing of the blade by the healing remedy thus influenced the remaining blood and the patient far away from the sword benefited, just as in modern radionic healing.

Today eyebrows are no longer raised at the idea of a television set monitoring pictures from the other side of the world, drawn out of empty space via a satellite dish. The principle of radionics is no different. It is just that the empty space from which the radionic practitioner receives the information is another, not yet fully understood, energy field.

THE SUBTLETIES OF RADIONIC ANALYSIS AND TREATMENT

Although radionic analysis can instantly identify the cause of a patient's ills, radionic treatment relies solely upon the recipient's ability to heal, and may take time. Formative structures within the patient will absorb and adjust to the radionic treatment, but the change may take a while to appear in the physical body. (Alterations occur in the electromagnetic fields within the body, unbeknown to the patient.) Radionics cannot be *felt*, just as we cannot see or hear the forces that control the world of living form. To explain these invisible forces, I want to take you on an imaginary journey that will challenge some common assumptions about sight and sound and what is real and unreal.

Imagine you are walking through a forest and a strong wind is blowing. Suddenly there is a creaking, cracking sound and a large tree submits to the force of the wind and falls to the ground. Did you actually see the wind fell the tree? No.

You only saw the effect of the wind upon the tree; no one can see the actual movement of air, only its effect upon an object. Secondly, did you hear the noise as the tree fell? Yes, you did. But what if you were not in the forest at the time? Was there a sound as the tree fell to the ground? In truth, you cannot answer this question. If no observer exists to witness an event we do not know what has happened. Only if an observer has placed an instrument to record such events do we know that there has been a sound.

If no person or piece of equipment exists in the forest, the tree may have fallen in complete silence, or it could have made a sound; we will never know. The action of the wind (atoms of air moving at speed) interacted with the atomic structure of the tree, which failed to bend and absorb the force of the air. If the event was observed by the atomic structures of the observer's ears and eyes the movement and sound would have been interpreted electrically in the darkness and silence of the observer's brain. The interpretation lies wholly within the observer's mind and depends on what the observer expects to see or hear. So, if a tree falls in a forest does it make a noise? The answer is yes, and the answer is also no.

The unseen energy fields around the body control the atoms that make up its structures, and these structures contain all the information a radionic practitioner requires to assess a patient's health. Science has already established that individual atoms contain information – in the form of DNA – about the whole structure of the human body. In the 1950s, when Francis Crick was unravelling the double helix of DNA, he was also looking for an explanation as to why a wounded organism (such as an earthworm) should recreate its structure and functions exactly as they existed before it was damaged. We might just as well ask: how do our bodies know how to heal a cut finger, or how to repair a sports injury or a twisted ankle? It appears to happen all by itself.

The information required must already exist within us. We know that the chromosomes of all living organisms are composed of the same chemical substance and use the same system of code – the genetic information contained in one cell is therefore thought to be identical in all cells in that organism. But, in that case, how can cells specialise? How do they know when to repair bone, when to coagulate blood, and when to send immune cells to the site of a wound? And how do the billions of cells that all magically evolved from one fertilised egg mystically know how to create the human form and become muscle cells or blood cells or any other type of cells?

Questions such as these perhaps explain why there is today a groundswell of opinion among many biologists, scientists and doctors that molecular biology has reached its limits. The intelligence that shapes elemental matter into organic forms is the most profound mystery of life – the possible existence of a silent language of thoughtstrings within and around the structures of our bodies has to be considered. When a radionic practitioner poses mental questions about the status of the physical organism during an assessment, it is this subtle intelligence existing within the cells of the human body that provides the answers.

A single cell or a balanced atomic structure within a hair sample contains all the information the practitioner needs about the whole structure. The fact is that the body contains billions of cells that all came from just one cell. Practising radionics successfully therefore requires medical knowledge of the human form, familiarity with subtle anatomy, and esoteric knowledge, plus an understanding of the principles of quantum physics.

All chemistry is based on quantum physics and energy fields. Biological life can also be explained in this way, as can the behaviour of complex elements, molecules such as proteins and DNA itself. Clearly, to gain a complete picture of human life and its requirements when diseased, medical practitioners should study all three philosophies: biology, chemistry and quantum physics.

With this background, orthodox doctors would have a much better understanding of the origins of life, wellbeing and acquired health, and would certainly be more competent to heal the sick. In my opinion, until the teaching of quantum physics becomes part of orthodox medical studies, the resources of health services around the world will continue to be extended beyond their limits and ill-health will continue to spread.

THE SUBTLE ANATOMY

When conducting a radionic analysis to discover the cause of a patient's illness, the practitioner needs to examine the subtle anatomy. As we know, electromagnetic energy fields control the functioning of all living organisms. It is therefore on this subtle level that the information exists to establish the cause of the effects felt in the physical body.

The word 'aura' is commonly used to describe an energy field surrounding the physical body, sometimes at a distance of no more than a few inches. This can be measured with special electrically sensitive instruments, which can relay the observed electric fields to a video display unit showing how far the field of energy extends around the patient as well as what colour it is. In radionics this field of energy is known as the physical-etheric body and it surrounds the whole of the physical form.

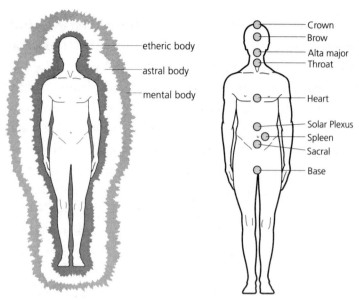

Figure 8 Diagrams showing the three major energy fields around the human body and the chakra system.

In Figure 8, the etheric body is shown closest to the physical body, together with two other energy fields marked as the emotional and mental bodies. The word 'body' is used in its loosest sense, to describe a field of energy surrounding the physical body. In addition, there are circles depicting energy centres, or chakras, that relate to physical endocrine glands. The chakras (or energy vortices) are connected by pathways of energy in the form of meridians. And these energy pathways transmit thoughts from chakra to chakra, through the mental and emotional bodies, enabling attitudes and attributes to be experienced throughout, on the physical, emotional and mental levels.

This explains why emotional stress and trauma can affect the performance of a gland or organ system in the body. Data has been gathered recording which thoughts and attitudes affect which part of the body and allow an illness to manifest. Students of radionics are taught which areas of the subtle body to examine and from which energy centres to obtain readings for the purposes of analysis and subsequent treatment. When conducting an assessment practitioners methodically pose specific mental questions to themselves about the subtle counterpart of particular areas of the physical body, which can cause many and varied symptoms on the physical level. The answers to the questions are transmitted via a pendulum.

THE PENDULUM

Analysis is carried out by measuring degrees of deviation from the norm in whichever area of the subtle anatomy the practitioner is examining or questioning. The information is gathered from the patient's hair sample which is linked with the radionic instrument and the practitioner's mind energy. The measuring tool used over the analysis instrument is usually a pendulum (see Figure 9). This replaced the stick-pad used in the early instruments described in Chapter 1. The movement of the pendulum held by the radionic

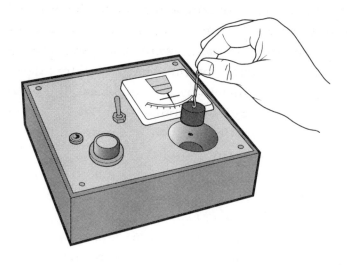

Figure 9 A typical pendulum being held over a student training instrument.

practitioner is influenced by the questions posed in the practitioner's mind. The pendulum itself has no direct way of accessing the subtle body information; this is done by the thought processes of the practitioner. The pendulum is held over the instrument and the measurements are noted. (For more on this, see page 77.)

The radionic process is actually instantaneous mind-to-mind transference of information. The instrument itself has no direct influence on the information gathered. This is why radionic instruments can be powered by electricity, magnetism or light photons, or they can be portable with no internal power at all. Instruments can have a stick-pad or an exterior

pendulum used over the sample – energised by
the operator for making actual measurements – it
makes no difference. All types of instruments will
work for practitioners who are versed in their
particular use.

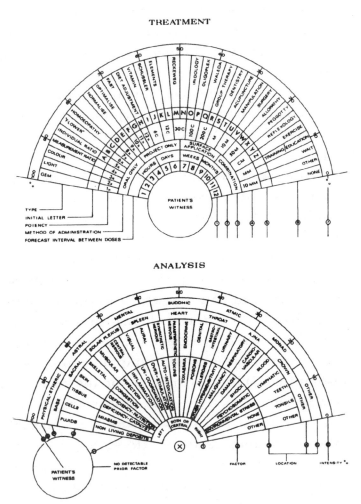

Figure 10 Chart boards used on the Malcolm Rae Analysis
and Treatment Instrument.

The real power source for all types of radionic instruments, both for assessment and treatment, is mind energy. Knowledge of physics and subtle anatomy, along with complete medical, physiological and biological training, are therefore essential. And this is why open-minded doctors make the best radionic practitioners. It all started with Dr Abrams, continued with Dr Ruth Drown and culminated in the last century with Dr Westlake and Dr David Tansley, all of them radionic practitioners of repute and writers of books used in radionic schools across the world.

Radionics is also possible without a pendulum, using a computer program based on radionic procedures and philosophy (for more on this, see Chapter 8). Information about the patient is entered into the computer and a complete subtle anatomy profile is produced on that patient. This program also displays the patient's optimum and inherent levels of chakra activity. When this is compared with the patient's case history and symptoms the cause of the symptoms can easily be identified. With this information the doctor or practitioner can then use a radionic instrument to treat the patient and prepare simulated homeopathic or energetic remedies to be given orally. This form of radionics appeals to many people because it does not rely upon learning to use a pendulum, something that many prospective students find difficult.

Chapter 4

Radionic Practitioners

HISTORICALLY, RADIONICS has been portrayed as a therapy practised by people who possess some magical gift of healing. They are known to use 'black boxes' with hair or blood samples from patients who then mysteriously get better without taking any medicine or having any contact with the mystical person.

The truth is that, ever since the days of the eminent American researcher and practitioner Dr Ruth Drown, the orthodox medical profession has vilified radionics. Because practitioners have been forced to remain clandestine for so many years, there has been little publicity about this method of healing. However, change is on the way. The late twentieth century saw the radionic fraternity beginning to edge out of the closet, and the public and other healthcare professionals are gradually becoming more interested in this enigmatic and esoteric therapy. Three basic categories of radionic practitioners have emerged, all of whom have an important contribution to make.

The first of these categories is the lay practitioner, often working part-time. This category includes dowsers (who use pendulums) and others who may prefer to call their practice medical radiesthesia and will often provide it free of charge.

These practitioners frequently make use of extra-sensory perception (ESP) and do medical dowsing over hair samples and medical books and charts. They have normally passed examinations in subtle anatomy and they usually belong to radionic or dowsing organisations as associate members. I have met may such dedicated, self-taught practitioners who perform excellent work.

Secondly, there are professional full-time practitioners who are full members of radionic associations and have satisfied examining boards of their competence in both human biology and subtle anatomy. They perform radionic analysis and treatment of patients and hold indemnity insurance. This category of practitioner will usually analyse the cause of the patient's symptoms relative to the subtle anatomy analysis. They are inclined not to give their own diagnosis, normally relying upon the diagnosis passed on from the patient's doctor or consultant.

A number of practitioners advertise the fact that they treat animals. Veterinary surgeons often refer patients to these practitioners, whose expertise in animal subtle anatomy enables them to make a diagnosis and analysis in cases with very few observable symptoms.

The third category are the fully qualified medical doctors, veterinary surgeons and complementary healthcare professionals, well-versed in medical science and subtle anatomy, who use radionics as a primary diagnostic and treatment procedure. This latter category are skilled in diagnosis and prescribing for the physical body with homeopathy, herbs, vitamins and minerals or nutrition, whilst also treating the causative factors in a patient's illness with radionics.

These professional radionic practitioners can make their own diagnosis of the patient's symptoms and will not usually rely upon an orthodox diagnosis which may or may not be accurate.

How to find a radionic practitioner

There are two good ways to obtain the services of a competent radionic practitioner. One is by following a recommendation from a successfully treated patient; the other is by contacting one of the professional complementary medicine organisations that keep registers of qualified practitioners. Make sure your chosen practitioner has indemnity insurance and carefully examine the literature he or she sends you with the questionnaire to complete.

Some patients like to meet their chosen practitioner for an initial consultation. However, this is by no means essential as your radionic practitioner can be anywhere in the world. I have patients in many other countries as well as locally, and I know of radionic practitioners in the USA who have patients here in the UK.

The most successful radionic practitioners I have met are multi-disciplined, with established careers in medicine or complementary medicine (such as homeopathy, chiropractic, osteopathy, herbalism or nutrition). However, the best practitioners are definitely those with a medical background. Doctors who are completely familiar with the workings of the physical body can easily understand the subtle workings of the cells and are able to comprehend how the energy fields can be treated. Most importantly, a doctor or trained healthcare professional can immediately recognise the symptoms of serious illnesses.

I have seen and heard radionic practitioners claim a set of symptoms to be an imbalance of an energy field in a physical, etheric or mental body area and recommend radionic treatment alone. Meanwhile, the patient is suffering a collapse of the central nervous system and needs urgent medical intervention.

Initially those interested in finding a radionic practitioner should contact either the

Institute for Complementary Medicine in London or the Radionic Association near Oxford for further information (see Useful Addresses).

SHOULD YOU TELL YOUR DOCTOR?

When you have chosen your radionic practitioner do you tell your doctor or current healthcare professional? This presents patients with a dilemma, as telling your doctor may well give rise to comments such as 'what a waste of time and money'. However, my personal opinion is that a patient's current medical practitioner should be told. Show your doctor all the information you have been given, even tell them about other related reading material (such as this book), and when the assessment is complete tell your doctor what the treatment involves.

There are several good reasons to be open about your radionic treatment. Firstly, how else will other disciplines in medicine learn about radionics? And, more importantly, not telling your doctor misleads him in his interpretation and further prescribing for your progress and recovery. For instance, your doctor may prescribe a drug that has absolutely no effect, while your alternative healthcare practitioner has provided you with treatment that is aiding your recovery. Withholding this information from your doctor as you get better will make him believe the totally ineffectual remedy is actually working. He may then be more inclined to prescribe it for future patients who are receiving no other form of healthcare.

So, when you have chosen your radionic practitioner tell your current doctor if you are receiving their treatment, whatever favourable or unfavourable comments he or she makes. Patients often tell me that blood tests and scans have shown a marked improvement in their health and that consultants and doctors have been amazed at their recovery. I ask if they have told the doctor about their radionic treatment. 'Oh no, I could not possibly have done that,' they say. Unfortunately, this attitude does nothing to benefit patients in general or the medical profession. Say it as it really is. It's your body, your life, and the adverse comments you may receive should not deflect you from your chosen path to health and wellbeing.

WHAT HAPPENS WHEN YOU CONSULT A RADIONIC PRACTITIONER?

Once your mind is made up and you confirm your acceptance of the radionic practitioner's terms you will receive a case history questionnaire to complete. This will of course vary between practitioners but should be similar to the one shown on pages 70–1.

This is just an example to show the type of information required by the practitioner. The more information you provide, the more accurately the practitioner will be able to establish the cause of the symptoms. The information on your case history questionnaire will be compared with the results of the subtle anatomy analysis (see Chapter 5). By correlating the two (i.e. identifying the physical manifestation with the subtle causes), the radionic practitioner will decide upon the appropriate treatment. This may be pure radionic treatment at a distance via the same hair sample used to establish the cause of the symptoms (see Chapter 6). Or the practitioner may decide upon oral medication as a supplement to radionic projection or broadcast. Or he or she may opt for some other form of natural therapy.

Many practitioners will telephone their patients when the analysis is complete. They will tell them what remedy to buy, explain that radionic treatment has begun, and start charging on a monthly basis. My personal approach is to give the patient a full typed report of my findings and to outline the medication to be used (I organise this by sending prescriptions to the required pharmacies). The advantage of a written report is that the patient has a tangible record to refer to at any time as the treatment proceeds.

Patients should also participate in the healing process by sending their practitioner monthly reports on their progress. Some doctors

Private and Confidential

CASE HISTORY
Date ....

Surname .... Mr/Mrs/Ms or other title.................

Maiden name (if applicable)....................... Forename/s ....

Address ....

....

Tel no. .... Fax no...

Introduced by..

Date of birth .... Country of birth ....

Height .... Weight..

Occupation .... Marital status ....

No. of children and their ages...

Recreational interests..

Is your blood pressure high, low or normal?...

Coffee – no. of cups per day? ....

Tea – no. of cups per day?..

Other fluid intake per day: Alcohol.......... Fruit juice......... Water.........

Usual type of diet – general, vegetarian or vegan? ....

Cigarettes – no. per day ....

Tendency to colds/flu? No. per year.............. Recent X-rays? ....

Operations and approximate dates?..

Recent vaccinations?..

Other reasons for hospital visits? ....

Radionic Practitioners

Have you suffered any of the following? (Circle the relevant conditions)

Asthma	Bronchitis	Diabetes	Jaundice	Hepatitis
Insomnia	Constipation	Irritable bowel	Headaches	Migraines
Hay fever	Pleurisy	Pneumonia	Urinary conditions	
Skin conditions	Arthritis	Prostate conditions	PMT	
Rheumatism	Thyroid conditions	Other........................		

Does your mother or father suffer from any of the above?......................

Are your parents still alive? ....
If not, at what age did they pass away and why? ....

Please list any orthodox drugs you are taking, or have taken during the last twelve months ....

Please list your present symptoms...

Please list any other symptoms suffered during the last twelve months

....

Date of onset of the symptoms ....

Date of your last medical examination ....

Orthodox medical diagnosis and prognosis..

Your doctor's name and address ....

....

Are you taking any other treatments (i.e. complementary medicine)?
Please give details ....

Do you take regular vitamins? Please give daily doses...........................

Please describe your temperament..

....

Other comments you feel are important...

....

get their patients to complete weekly records of their observable symptoms and reactions to treatment and then send these to the practitioner. Whether or not one follows such a formal system, regular communication between practitioner and patient is essential for successful treatment.

I have a doctor friend who uses radionics in his practice and sets his patients 'homework' (to observe changes, and make notes of reactions during the treatment period). When they arrive for the next consultation he immediately asks them to please show him the homework. If the patient has been diligent then all is well. If not, they are sent away and told not to come back until it is complete. When I first heard about this approach I was a little taken aback, but he assures me it works wonders. His success rate has apparently increased by 50 per cent since he started taking this rigorous line with his patients!

It is not essential for radionic practitioners to have consulting rooms or clinics in the high street, as radionics is normally conducted in the quiet of an office or study. Patients are unaware of what actually happens during the analytical procedures, and usually receive the results by mail or e-mail. To rectify this, I have outlined two types of analysis in Chapter 5. One is the traditional system, using instruments, charts and a pendulum; the other uses a computer program to establish the cause of the patient's symptoms.

1. This radionic nine-dial analysis and treatment instrument is particularly interesting, because it contains the rectangular rubber diaphragm (see bottom right) that Ruth Drown devised for measuring certain reactions.
(see p27)

2. A very early radionic diagnostic instrument similar to that developed by radionics' founding father, Albert Abrams.

3. Dr Albert Abrams (1863–1924), one of the earliest radionics pioneers, whose fascination with radionics began whilst he was performing a routine abdominal examination.

4. Ruth Drown (d.1966) was one of the most successful of Abram's successors. Her work refining his groundbreaking techniques led to the discovery that radionics could work at a distance by replacing the human subject in the circuit with a sample of their hair or blood.

5. A radionics treatment instrument with an interrupter. This enables sedation (e.g. to ease a patient's headache) or stimulation (e.g. to promote healing), by pulsing the vibration over the patient's hair sample.

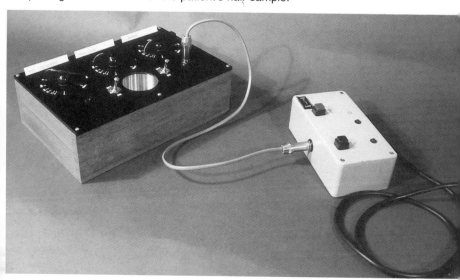

6. A Rae Analysis instrument showing the chart board attached to the main instrument. The hair sample is placed on the small circle on the left of the chart board and readings are taken using a pendulum.

7. This AST (Analysis, Simulate and Treatment) instrument, designed by Keith Mason, allows for both the preparation of remedies for oral use and for radionic treatment after the assessment.

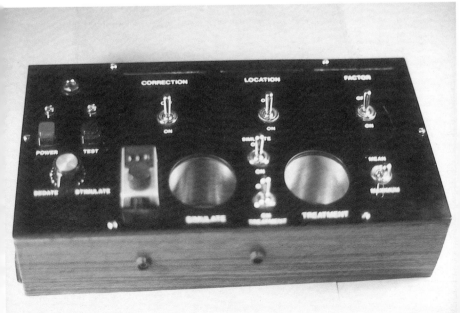

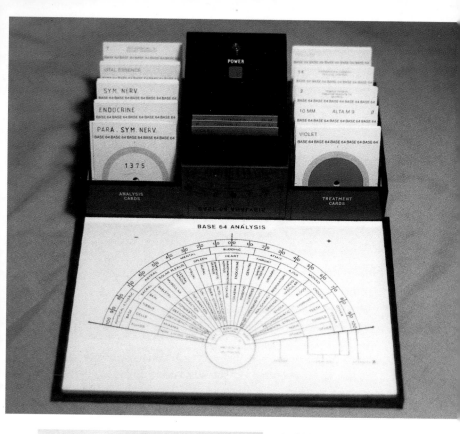

8. A Base Sixty-Four analysis instrument designed by Keith Mason, showing the card system with the central opening through which light photons are fired on to a hair sample placed on the analysis chart board.

9. A Base Sixty-Four biophoton instrument which also utilises light photons fired through specially designed cards either to treat a hair sample placed in the receiving chamber or to activate unpotentised tablets for oral use. This instrument is used extensively in South American teaching hospitals.

There are of course many different types of radionic instruments and systems in use throughout the world. The systems described in this guide are typical of those taught in British schools of radionics. I have also devised my own type of computerised radionic assessment, based on years of traditional radionic analysis and research. But it should be remembered that not all practitioners will use the systems I describe.

HOW DO YOU BECOME A RADIONIC PRACTITIONER?

Many successfully treated patients are so inspired by the benefits of radionic treatment that they want to learn more, and perhaps even become practitioners themselves. Radionics can be a very rewarding career but it takes time to complete the training and establish oneself as a professional full-time radionic practitioner. For all these reasons, a degree of commitment and persistence will be required.

There are a number of schools of radionics which offer a range of courses to suit the needs of prospective students. One of the best-known courses is run by the Radionic Association (see Useful Addresses) and this leads to a professional qualification.

The Radionic Association in Great Britain was founded in 1943. It is one of the principal professional bodies representing radionic practitioners and has strict standards and codes of conduct. Qualified members of the Radionic Association will have the letters M.Rad.A. after their name. The Radionic Association governs the School of Radionics which currently offers three courses: a three-year part-time course leading to the qualification of M.Rad.A., concentrating on humans; a short further course (for holders of the M.Rad.A.) which leads to a qualification to treat small animals and horses; and a further two-year course for those directly interested in soil and crops.

All of these courses depend upon the proficient use of the pendulum and the skill of dowsing, which are taught at the very start of the introductory course. I believe a qualification in human biology is obligatory before enrolment, or a course in human biology needs to be undertaken at the same time.

I personally conduct courses for professional healthcare practitioners and doctors leading to certified qualification and membership of the Institute for Complementary Medicine. In addition, I run courses for people wishing to use medical dowsing as an adjunct to their own healthcare and that of their family and friends. This course does not lead to any qualification to practise.

The course for existing healthcare professionals runs for one year part-time, with two examinations each term and a final examination leading to membership of the British Register of Complementary Practitioners (B.R.C.P.) in Energy Medicine. Healthcare professionals will already hold qualifications in biology or physiology or be practising medical doctors. Laypersons wishing to learn more about medical dowsing for their own personal use only need some basic knowledge of biology and a keen interest in healthcare.

Readers wanting to find out about studying radionics in countries other than Britain are advised to contact the British Register of Complementary Practitioners or visit their website (see Useful Addresses).

Chapter 5

Radionic Analysis and Consultation

A TYPICAL RADIONIC PRACTICE room, whether in a clinic or in a practitioner's home, will have a number of treatment instruments on shelves or stands, as the practitioner may have twenty or more patients on distant treatment at any one time. (Patients on daily radionic projection will be on an automatic instrument that treats up to a hundred patients' samples every few hours.) However, those patients requiring specialised radionic treatment will be given projections individually. Each treatment is set up for the exact causation determined by the practitioner at the time of analysis. These treatments are usually given once or twice a day and can last for anything from a few minutes up to fifteen minutes, depending on the severity of the illness. There will be fewer analysis instruments, as a practitioner can only perform one analysis at a time. Analysis instruments can vary in size. Imagine a suitcase standing on a desk – this would be the size of an electrically powered instrument from twenty or more years ago. The more up-to-date instruments tend to be much smaller – the size of a child's shoebox, energised by circular magnets, and easily portable.

Plate 1 shows a typical larger-style analysis instrument with rows of numerically inscribed dials where the practitioner sets the rates (the special sequences of numbers that represent the physical or subtle body areas being assessed). The practitioner will have a rate book containing hundreds of individual numerical rates representing organ functions, glands and all the individual body parts. These enable the practitioner to measure the degree of deviation from optimum function of the area denoted by the numerical sequence of numbers. The degree of deviation is indicated by the swing of the pendulum over a scale, in response to questions being posed in the practitioner's mind. This scale is normally marked zero to 100 and the degree of deviation is noted on a record sheet.

The sample of hair from the patient is sometimes placed in the centre of the scale where the measurement takes place or it is connected to the scale by a wire running from the plate on which the sample rests. The time-consuming part of the process is that the dials have to be re-set to measure each part of the body.

This type of instrument, using the rate system, can be used to treat the patient at a distance. This is done by simply flicking a switch from analysis mode to projection mode and then dialling up the rate for the area requiring the healing vibration. Again, this can be a time-consuming operation. In the early days of radionics, analysis could take many hours, making it financially non-viable.

It was the researcher Malcolm Rae who devised a speedier process using reference cards with the pattern or numerical rate embossed upon them. The instruments he developed only required the card to be dropped into a slot and the measurement taken. Plate 6 shows the smaller, Rae-type instrument, with the analysis chart connected to the main body of the instrument. The treatment instrument is of a similar size, energised by circular magnets, and has been in use for more than twenty years. Plate 9 shows a more modern, light photon (or biophotonic) instrument.

This instrument is used extensively in the USA, Australia and in France, mostly in private practices of healthcare professionals and some doctors. However, in Bogota it is used in the main teaching hospital for childhood illnesses with great success. The reason for the success is that the medical doctors in the Bogota teaching hospital are very spiritual and have a profound interest and belief in radionic philosophy and esoteric principles.

A MOTHER AND DAUGHTER PROBLEM

In May 1999 I treated a Swedish woman called Anna who was suffering from breast cancer. I found the causes of her illness to be of a subtle nature within the mental and emotional body areas, with profound stresses affecting the function of certain chakra or energy centres. However, she knew nothing of radionics or its philosophy and appeared rather orthodox in her approach to life. I therefore avoided using any esoteric jargon in my report. Practitioners have to be sensitive to their patients and express their findings accordingly.

I began by finding out more about her family situation, using ESP on the radionic instrument. (This can enable a practitioner to make very specific investigations based on a hunch or gut feeling about the causes of a patient's condition.)

In the report I sent her I said:

> A contributory cause to the breast cancer was I
> believe an emotional worry, perhaps with one
> of your daughters, and it was a period of your
> life where you had some difficulty in
> communicating your true feelings about a

certain situation. In this type of radionics we are able to establish the way a patient will react to stress and anxiety and about a year before the breast condition evolved I think you may have experienced the emotional stress with a daughter to which I am referring.

The radionic assessment of the hair sample provides both physical profiles of the elements within the body and at the same time a psychological profile, which includes your attributes and attitudes to life. The assessment shows you to be a very caring and loving person, and to those in your family and those close to you emotionally you can become totally devoted. However, it is very important that those people you bestow your love upon, also give back to you the same in return. If this is not forthcoming then inner stress will build up, affecting the way cells of the body metabolise, just as a worried businessman will develop a gastric ulcer through business stresses. Because I feel the stress or anxiety concerned the love of one of your children, and although you are normally a very wilful person in getting your own way, in this instance your own will was over-ridden. You could not say what you felt, and even if you did, the person you were so concerned about did not listen. You are a very intuitive and perceptive person and could see what mistakes would be made and this added to your inner frustration.

> The type of stress I have mentioned, and I can only surmise what went on, caused the magnesium elements.in your body to stop metabolising correctly. Because this element is a calcium channel regulator, the calcium elements and the red cells, along with the essential iron for the oxygenation of cells, began to deteriorate. The breast was the first area to be affected, due to the emotional and motherhood connection of the stress. It appears mothers often experience physical symptoms in the breast area when the stress is related to mother-child relationships, as the breast is the natural comforter to a child.

Having treated many women with breast lumps over the years, I believe their formation is largely due to subtle mental and emotional causes. The breast provides nourishment for a woman's children when young, but in later life it still has this vital energy even if the hormonal ability to provide nourishment has passed. A mother will use the breast to comfort a young child; and this is superseded in later years by hugging the child. Later still, when children leave home, the mother is no longer able to provide them with sustenance and protection. This can make her feel impotent and frustrated.

Worry and anxiety abound about the young adult now going out into the world, and the mother's breast is no longer a vital symbol in her life. Breast lumps are often linked to a lack of adaptability to changing circumstances. Adaptability and fluidity are essential to prevent the natural fibrin coming out of solution and causing fibrous tissue and breast lumps to develop. For more on this, refer to my book *Thoughts that Harm, Thoughts that Heal* (see Further Reading).

Anna's report continued:

> The next thing to happen was the fibrin in the body came out of solution, due to the poor action of the element of potassium chloride in the body and fibrous tissue began to develop. This, along with calcification of the tissue, showed as a tumour and this was the beginning of the whole saga. The magnesium levels are still poor and this is why the calcium is leaking from the bone and there has been a spread to the bones. What is very important is to correct the magnesium metabolism so that calcium will be absorbed correctly from your diet and will be held in the bone system.
>
> I am going to send with this report a couple of pages outlining some thoughts to overcome stress and some advice on what foods to eat. In addition I give some detail about your optimum potential and your strengths of character, as this is so important for you to hold in mind. To know yourself and your capabilities is to heal yourself. I do not know if the special supplements I wish to prescribe are available in

Sweden so I will give you the names of the products you need and the UK telephone numbers on a separate sheet. You will have to mention my name as the prescribing physician.

These remedies and supplements will have no adverse reaction with any orthodox treatment you decide to undertake, whether surgery or chemotherapy, nor will the radionic projections via the hair sample that I have just started. I will do this for about a week, but I do feel that a month at least is going to be needed to start the healing process and to get the absorption of the minerals and elements correct. I am enclosing a form of acceptance should you require me to conduct this service ...

Anna's case was of great interest because the subtle cause started due to poor communication and the ensuing stress that occurred when her daughter was in her late teens. This I established from the radionic assessment of Anna's hair sample, as measurements taken showed the throat and heart energy centres were congested at both a mental and emotional level.

Due to the stress connected to her child and the developing difficulty in their relationship, her physical body no longer absorbed elemental minerals properly. Radionic analysis of the physical structures showed the resulting elemental deficiencies, which led to the formation of the breast lump. But the lump was clearly a physical manifestation of a subtle cause. This is the advantage of radionic analysis over many other natural therapies: unseen causes of illness can be detected and exposed.

Anna had surgery to remove the lump and continued her programme of supplements and remedies for about three months. The last report she sent me suggested she was feeling much better and that communication with her daughter was now more harmonious. This will assist the restoration of the throat and heart energy centres to the correct level. And, coupled with the radionic projections, which I gave her for two months, should prevent any further malignancy.

SUBTLE ANATOMY ANALYSIS

If patients are to receive regular radionic projections – whether daily or a few times a week over a month – it is important to obtain their approval first. I therefore send prospective patients an acceptance form which explains how radionic analysis and treatment are carried out. I do not commence treatment until they have given their agreement.

When performing an assessment, I place the hair sample upon the analysis chart and take readings (using the pendulum) of the nine energy centres. In each case I establish a reason or causal factor for the deviation I measure. The nine important energy centres or chakras (see Figure 8) are each measured in the three subtle body areas – etheric, emotional and mental.

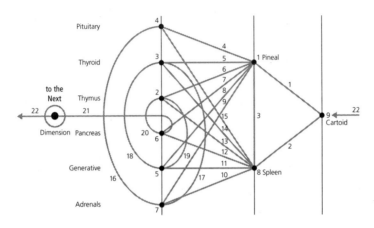

Figure 11 Twenty-two pathways and ten energy centres all having positive and negative vibrations creating sixty-four dimensions of energy, being the blueprint for life.

In addition to the physical areas (below) of the body which are influenced by the chakra or energy centres there are causal mental and emotional factors that work through the energy centres. The centres contain definite and recognisable attributes and attitudes which allow the practitioner to determine what type of stress has affected the patient when illness arises in a particular area of the body. The list on page 87 gives a brief description of these influences.

THE NINE MAJOR ENERGY CENTRES

Centre	Location	Physical gland	Area governed
Crown	Above the top of the head	Pineal	Right creative brain, right eye and the right side of the head
Brow	Between the eyes	Pituitary	Left brain, left eye, ears, nose, sinuses, nervous system
Throat	The neck	Thyroid	Bronchial, vocal, lungs, alimentary tract
Heart	Sternum (centre of the ribs)	Thymus	Heart, circulation, blood, immune system, vagus nerve
Solar plexus	Above the waist	Pancreas	Stomach, liver, gall bladder, nervous system
Sacral	Below the waist	Gonads	Reproductive system
Base	Apex of sacrum (base of the spine)	Adrenal	Spinal column, kidneys, locomotor system
Spleen	Left of navel	Spleen	Blood and skin
Alta major	Base of occiput (between the top of the neck and the base of the skull)	Carotid plexus	Blood pressure, fluids

THE CAUSAL FACTORS

Centre	Causal factors
Crown	Intuition and perception, willpower, confidence, diplomacy
Brow	Logic and discrimination, kindness and affection
Throat	Intellect and communication, philosophical outlook
Heart	Love and understanding, patience and calmness
Solar plexus	Wisdom and devotion, loyalty and respect
Sacral	Justice, accuracy, traditional views
Base of spine	Willpower, very strong ideals and determination
Spleen	Mental and emotional balance and stability
Alta major	Profound thinking, arbitration and planning

A NUTRITION PROBLEM

Not all patients have deeper mental and emotional issues as causes of their symptoms. For instance, the case of James Bradstone, a baby of eighteen months, shows the efficacy of radionics in establishing causes in the cell structures and nutritional levels (including amino acids and vitamins). A major advantage of using radionics with young children is that information can be obtained that a young child would be incapable of providing.

James was failing to gain weight, suffering

from chronic constipation, and seemed to have little awareness of his surroundings. His parents believed they were facing a lifetime of having to support an undeveloped, brain-damaged child. The orthodox medical diagnosis of herpes simplex encephalitis was confirmed by my analysis. But I believed James's immune system must have been compromised in some way before his birth, allowing the invasion of the herpes virus. I therefore asked about Mrs Bradstone's state of health during her pregnancy. Had she been given ferrous sulphate or any other orthodox medication for anaemia, or any other malady, during her confinement?

Radionic assessment of James's hair sample showed a major deficiency of the amino acid L-Lysine. Lysine is an essential amino acid and has been found to have therapeutic effects in viral-related disease. Over the last ten years complementary medical practitioners have shown particular interest in the ability of L-Lysine to control the herpes virus. Insufficient intake leads to decrease in body weight, anaemia, and enzyme disorders, and it is used today with children suffering from stunted growth and gastric disturbances.

I therefore wrote to James's parents as follows:

> ... the use of L-Lysine will assist the chronic constipation and the major problem of the growth factor in the soft tissue cells not only of the brain but the whole body.

Lysine also plays a major role in bone growth by means of aiding calcium absorption, and assists the collagen integrity for the connective tissue of the brain. Lysine cannot be synthesised in the body and the breakdown of Lysine is not reversible; hence the major effect upon James when the virus interrupted the metabolic processes that allow absorption of Lysine . . .

In addition Vitamin E is essential for cell growth and muscle strength, along with the development of healthy brain tissue. In the past I have used large amounts of Vitamin E with children very successfully, particularly when mothers have taken iron supplementation at the request of their doctors.

Vitamin C in high doses is equally important for collagen production and the immune system, as well as tissues of bones, teeth and skin . . .

Start by giving James 500mg of Lysine per day crushed up in his drinks of juice; let's say over three drinks (not milk) during the day between his milk feeds. The Lysine can be increased over a period of four to six weeks, but only based upon his reaction if any and by chatting to me before you increase the dosage.

Vitamin E to be given in liquidised food such as fish, lamb or organic chicken. Pierce the capsule, empty the contents into his food and give 250i.u. per day, increasing to 1000i.u.

within a two-month period.

Please order the 84 tablet size of Blackmores Elemental Celloid Mag-Cal-Plus. Crush a tablet and give three a day in juice or food. From the homoeopathic pharmacy order 14 grams of tablets of a special combination of Lycopodium 6(c) potency with Kali Phos 6(x) and Dr Bach Walnut . . .

Based upon your comments and James's progress after a month I would like to introduce a special Vitamin C complex. This contains stabilised mineral ascorbates to act as a precursor to soft tissue cells, but I wish to wait until James has the most important supplements within his system for a month at least.

If you have any questions please call me or write, and I would like to have a little history of Mrs Bradstone's confinement and any drugs taken. I would like a written report on James's progress after the first month, particularly in regard to his chronic constipation . . .

James began to gain weight after two months of radionic treatment, which I directed at the absorption processes of the amino acids and at the pituitary gland (as this gland, along with the pineal, is active in a child's early development). After six months of taking the supplements the parents reported a major change in his awareness of his surroundings. And after a year James is as normal as any two-year-old.

GIVING NATURE A LITTLE TIME

Not all cases we deal with in radionics are of a chronic or very serious nature, although it's true that radionics is often a last resort for those suffering apparently incurable illness. Life would be easier if we only had to deal with the many simple infections, stomach disorders and other minor illnesses that flood the waiting rooms of most orthodox doctors. However, many patients suffering this type of ailment would do well to allow their body's own defence mechanisms and regenerative powers to prevail for a few days, instead of immediately rushing for antibiotics or pain-killers. In addition, the hard-pressed health service would have more time to deal with the more seriously ill patients.

When patients come to me for a consultation I often ask them to take a few minutes to consider the marvellous qualities their body possesses which are all too often ignored. Let me now ask you, the reader, to do the same. Contemplate the structure of your body, the skin cells, the soft tissue cells, the nervous system and bony structure, and how it all developed into billions of cells from that one fertilised egg at your conception. Ask yourself what conscious part you played in its growth and development. The truthful answer has to be none; it all happened by itself.

The cells of your body have a mind of their own; they control the functions that maintain you, hopefully, in a state of wellbeing (remember, your body always wants to be well and perform at its optimum level). We must recognise, however, that we have a personality and free will that can consciously direct our body to perform physical tasks. Our personality also makes mental and emotional demands for our interaction with our fellow human beings. But over the actual maintenance and restructuring of the body, the accomplishment of self-repair and self-reproduction, we have no conscious dominion. Our body has a mind of its own. It knows what to do.

For example, if you injure yourself at work or in the garden you don't consciously send platelets (cells that cause the blood to coagulate) to the site of the wound to stem the blood flow. You don't panic and think to yourself 'I hope the blood doesn't start clotting in my heart valves'. The body just gets on with the required job, and only at the injured location.

In addition, immune cells appear to counter infection, and the skin begins to close over the wound. This provides a protective layer, formed in conjunction with the coagulated blood, which in turn forms the scab.

Clearly, our cells know what to do to accomplish healing, but their capabilities go a lot further; they can also make long-term changes in the body to compensate for the many challenges we face throughout our lives. The body can adapt to changes in diet, environment, stress and anxiety; it can identify toxins, bacteria and viruses; it can recognise and instantly make adjustment to body structures or activate an army of defence cells when threatened by an aggressor. In addition it provides us with a 'flight or fight' mechanism when we are under threat.

But there are times when this self-protective capacity within us fails, illness takes hold, and our cells lose their ability to heal. At such times, there has to be a reason or special cause why you have become ill and your cells have failed to perform their allotted task. And this is what must be examined, not only by the doctor or healthcare practitioner, but by patients themselves.

The innate intelligence and healing ability of our cells appears to be within the vibration of the electromagnetic fields that control the function and form of cells. If the body knows how to heal but fails to do so, the reason for the failure must also exist in this same electromagnetic field. The use of radionic analysis has many distinct advantages over other complementary therapies in that it delves into the unseen electromagnetic fields where illness and disease arise. Radionics can therefore treat in these subtle areas, which allows healing action to be taken in preventing disease before it actually manifests itself in recognisable symptoms.

IDENTIFYING NON-LOCAL EFFECTS

When it comes to assessing patients, radionics is particularly effective at identifying non-local effects. For instance, at an initial consultation an orthodox doctor will ask the patient, 'Where does it hurt?' If the patient has severe migraine, and drugs and pain relievers prove ineffective, the patient may eventually be sent to a neurologist. Or, if the doctor considers there is a psycho-somatic factor, maybe a psychiatrist will be consulted. With orthodox medicine no account is taken of the whole patient. For kidney pains you see a urologist; for a skin problem you see a dermatologist; for pains in the chest you see a cardiologist.

However, some conditions result in very obvious external symptoms but have very specific internal causes. A good example of one of these conditions is eczema (a flaky, itchy skin inflammation which can cause a great deal of pain and discomfort). In my thirty years of radionic and naturopathic medicine I have cured many cases of eczema by treating the patient's liver.

This may sound strange, but not many people realise that the skin is actually an organ used by the body to rid itself of toxins (especially fatty acids). Improve digestion and liver function and eczema will dissipate. In addition I often use homeopathic remedies and nutritional changes for eczema treatment. (Babies with skin symptoms can be given homeopathic medicine via their mothers if they are being breast-fed.)

Seven-year-old Charlotte had suffered from eczema since babyhood, and came to see me with weeping wounds in her elbow joints and on the backs of her legs. Radionic analysis showed poor liver function and an allergy to dairy products, I also asked for a hair sample from her mother as she suffered from asthma, and asthma and skin conditions are often linked through genetic transference mother–child.

I gave Charlotte remedies for the liver, removed all dairy products from her diet and provided large doses of elemental celloids to include potassium and calcium fluoride. I gave radionic projections to the solar plexus and the liver in particular by using special rates and the colour projection of violet. Here was a typical case of a non-local effect – the digestive problem causing skin symptoms. Her previous orthodox treatment was to apply as much steroid cream as possible to reduce the irritation. The skin specialist said she would grow out of the condition by the time she reached puberty, however by this time she would have had very little skin quality left!

After two months of treatment her physical condition improved by only about 50 per cent and the family became a little fretful that Charlotte was still missing school regularly due to the continuing skin irritation which still caused her to scratch. I was not going to change the prescription, but I did suggest some tolerance remedies. I also gave some radionic projections of the Dr Bach Flower Remedies and in addition Charlotte took the flower remedies orally night and morning.

Charlotte went back to school, and after six weeks she came running into my clinic to show me the inner folds of her elbows and the backs of her legs. She was so proud of her new skin, and the irritation was all gone.

Over the years, I have found that most skin conditions have to be treated from the inside. Treatment from the outside (with ointments and creams) only drives the condition deeper into the patient's constitution, often causing adverse effects in other parts of the body.

TREATING PATIENTS ON BOTH THE PHYSICAL AND SUBTLE LEVEL

Before the First World War many young people in the UK were treated radionically, obviously knowing nothing of the procedures, only hearing their parents say that a Mrs W. now had their hair sample and would be treating, say, their skin problem or their growing pains in the knees. Radionics was very popular amongst the aristocracy for some reason. They had a great belief in the system, even though little was really understood about the workings of the 'black box'.

It was one of these patients, now retired,

who contacted me from the south of France a few years ago after reading an article about my work published in a national newspaper. It turned out that he had known Mr and Mrs Wilcox and other founder members of the Radionic Association, including the late Miss Elizabeth Baerlein who died in 1982, and Mrs Lavender Dower. I was able to write back and tell him that Lavender was still exceedingly well and active in her radionic practice despite her ninety or more years (a very good advert for radionics).

He had also requested treatment for his psoriasis and had sent me a hair sample. I wrote to him as follows:

As requested I have conducted a radionic analysis with a view to treating the deeper underlying causes to the inveterate psoriasis you suffer. There is a definite pattern to the cause of the psoriasis, and that is a digestive factor that has been exacerbated by low-level but continual stress. The approach to the treatment is going to be twofold. Radionic projections on a daily basis to correct the formative patterns of the digestive process, and the epidermis layers of the skin and its nutrition. The other part of the treatment being a course of oral remedies that will be working at a more subtle level and will be working to eradicate the cause of the physical symptoms. The remedies required are combined in one tablet and are coming from me

> under separate cover and you will receive a
> remedy marked Berberis Aquifolium/Arsen
> Alb/Crab Apple and Beech. Please take 2 little
> pills on the tongue three times a day, away from
> meals by 10 minutes or so and a further dose at
> bedtime. Please let me know how you progress
> after the first month of treatment.

The remedy I recommended was actually a
combination of two homeopathic remedies and
two Dr Bach Flower Remedies. This complex or
combination remedy was simulated on an instrument similar to the one shown in plate 7.

SIMULATING REMEDIES

A conventional homeopathic remedy is produced
under pharmaceutical conditions by a process of
succussion (rhythmical shaking) and dilution
from a known substance and its potency will be
indicated by letters and numbers such as '6(x)' or
'6(c)'. According to professional homeopaths, a
remedy marked '23(x)' or higher contains no
measurable amount of the original substance and
is basically pure energy. This mystifying concept
(that a remedy could be effective despite containing no measurable quantity of the 'active
ingredient') led radionic researcher Malcolm Rae
to produce the first homeopathic simulator.
Using this instrument, he discovered that un-

potentised lactose used in the preparation of traditional homeopathic remedies could be made energetically potent by radionic influence.

To do this, he replaced the circular plate where the hair sample had been placed on a radionic projection instrument, with a small container where pills or fluids could receive the same vibration. He then gave these pills to his patients and they worked in the same manner as a homeopathic remedy. This simulation process allows complex remedies to be made within minutes and is particularly good for treating allergies.

For example, in 1999 a young woman suffering hay fever and rhinitis due to a pollen allergy consulted me for a radionic analysis just prior to the hay fever season. I confirmed her diagnosis and decided to make a remedy from the actual cause of her condition. Spring flowers appeared to be the main culprit, so I gathered the pollen from a few flowers, and placed it on a card used in a biophoton radionic instrument as shown in plate 9. When the power was switched on, the light photons passed through the centre aperture of the card, through the electromagnetic field of the pollen, and on to the reflective chamber where the un-potentised pills were placed. The pills then absorbed the simulated energy of the pollen, and when these were administered to the patient the allergy was relieved. The principle used was the same as that of homeopathy: like treating like.

Chapter 6

Radionic Treatment at a Distance

I RECALL A FEW YEARS AGO being woken very early one morning, around 4 am. 'Hello, I am so sorry to disturb you so early at home, but it's Margaret here. I'm in Australia as you know, on holiday, and I realise it's very early in the morning your time. I am sitting up in a hospital bed with severe tummy pains. They think it may be acute appendicitis and they want to do more tests as they can't find out what's wrong with me. Please, please put me on the black box.' I tell Margaret not to worry, I will put her on 'the box' right away. Reassured, she rings off and I go to the kitchen to make myself a cup of coffee.

Armed with my cup of caffeine (my only moderate addiction first thing in the morning), I find Margaret's hair sample in the files, place it on the radionic analysis instrument and scan for degrees of deviation against the known rates for various gastro-intestinal (GI) conditions. I find no appendicitis. However, after a few minutes, I find the rate for poisons indicated in the GI tract and, upon checking further, shellfish appears to be the problem. I do not have the telephone number of the hospital to advise her of my findings, so all I can do is set up a radionic treatment.

I use the Rae treatment instrument with the special cards to eliminate the poisons from the GI tract and I include treatment cards to enhance her general constitution and to reduce the pain and inflammation. I place Margaret's hair sample in the well of the instrument and start the projections. Many of the radionic treatment instruments have timers. Two or three minutes is the normal duration of the projection (or broadcast, as some people call it).

As I have already explained, each radionic treatment is effectively an EPR experiment. I want something specific to happen to Margaret on the other side of the earth. She has made the request. I have responded with a command in the instrument; eliminate the poisons from her body. Knowing what is wrong, the thoughts from my mind are activating the thoughts in her subconscious mind, and within the electromagnetic fields controlling the cell structures in the GI tract, and the healing will start. This is the thoughtstring phenomenon (the third particle or super-string, as physicists call it) providing a link between the two particles, one in the hair sample and the other within Margaret in Australia.

Margaret was treated on the instrument twice a day for just two days. I then conducted a brief check-up and found the readings greatly improved, with hardly any deviation from functional perfection at all. I considered she was feeling better and discontinued the treatment. While I was sitting at my desk the next morning, my one cup of coffee long gone, the phone rang.

'Hello, this is Margaret from Australia. I was discharged from hospital earlier today and I am back in my hotel. It's evening time now and I feel much better. They think it might have been food poisoning, but before they could do more tests I began to feel better and I discharged myself. What did you find?'

I told her of my findings. She was relieved, thanked me for the radionic treatment and confirmed again that she never goes anywhere in the world without my phone number. Now there's a compliment, not to me (although my wife is very understanding), but to radionics and the 'black box'.

TREATING THE CAUSAL FACTORS

In my years of radionic practice I have treated many asthma sufferers and have found that intellectuals in particular can sometimes develop asthma, which in turn leads to absent-mindedness, anxiety and panic attacks. This can manifest further as isolation and loneliness. A case that springs to mind was that of a well-respected lawyer who had given many years' service to the community. His overall health was excellent until the expansion of the law firm necessitated the appointment of an additional partner.

The new addition to the firm proved to be a threat to his stability, as more clients moved to the new associate and my patient found he could no longer express his true feelings and others in the firm would not listen to his viewpoint. He lost long-established clients and felt very lonely amongst his peers. His asthma was initially acute but soon became chronic. When the inhalers supplied by his physician started to prove less effective he consulted me.

I gave him natural remedies that provided him with more elasticity in the connective tissue and the muscles. In particular, I started daily radionic projections that gave him more tolerance of his work situation. I told him to speak more freely of his feelings to his wife and family and to seek out close friends who would listen to the whole story.

My advice was to accept change as part of his own evolution. In this situation within the law firm, he could use his accumulated knowledge to bring about change. This in turn would bring back his confidence. He would display conviction and others would once more believe in his competence. He took my advice and the natural remedies, I gave him radionic projections for two months and the asthma began to improve.

Then, some weeks later, I received a panicky telephone call. 'I have a very important case in court and this afternoon I am presenting a difficult foundation to an argument. I had it planned out in my mind yesterday. But I was awake most of the night and this morning, as you can hear, my asthma is appalling.'

I consulted my records of the causal factors in his case to establish the reasons for this acute attack. It was obvious that the build-up of stress before appearing in court had started the symptoms of the asthma again. I told my patient to rest assured that I would start radionic treatment straight away.

As an emergency treatment, I placed the hair sample on the biophoton instrument with cards in a specific order to relay an instruction to my patient to release the inner vexation and feelings of inadequacy and to restore complete confidence. I also used two other cards in the sequence of projection. One was the Dr Bach remedy Larch, and the other was the homeopathic remedy Kali Phos. This is often used as an oral remedy to relieve anxiety, but in this case I used the vibrational field of the card as an adjunct to complete projection of restoring confidence. I left this treatment working for two minutes at a time, at half-hour intervals during the afternoon.

That evening my patient rang, sounding very pleased with himself. The presentation had gone perfectly and there had been no sign of the asthma. In fact I had not used a card or rate for the asthma. Instead, I had used projections to counter the feelings of inadequacy that were linked to the original cause of the condition.

TREATING THE CHAKRAS OR ENERGY CENTRES

I was once consulted by a lecturer with thyroid gland problems. He had developed poor energy levels and was wondering whether he would be able to continue in his profession. This patient had a phobia about taking pills of any kind and had only reluctantly agreed to take thyroxin. My initial analysis showed some obvious stresses; I would have liked to administer some complementary therapy but this was not going to be possible.

Because the patient had some understanding of electronics and physics, I explained how radionics worked. I offered to treat the unseen energy levels of his throat chakra to enhance his communication abilities and this was agreed. I also prepared a radionic profile, outlining my theory as to the cause of the thyroid condition. Here is part of my report:

I wish to make the following comments and suggestions based upon my analysis and taking into consideration the results of the computer profile. You are, I believe, a person with strong ethics and principles and, as your profile suggests, both determined and creative. This would also apply to your career and I see by your completed case history that you are a lecturer by profession.

The radionic assessment is picking up stress related to the throat area at an energetic level, with an element of frustration present as a stress affecting cell metabolism (an example of which is the 'fight or flight' mechanism, wherein a shock or trauma produces a hormone response).

I am suggesting that over the past few months, and maybe as long as a year or so, you have experienced frustration in your work. This emanates from your strong beliefs, correct attitudes, creativity and principles being over-ridden by either the strong convictions of another person or group of persons, or alternatively you having to teach systems where you personally see serious flaws, incorrectness and possible wrongdoings. This is causing you inner frustration and is affecting the cell metabolism of the endocrine glands, particularly those of the throat and neck.

The patient agreed that a situation very similar to that I described had indeed taken place. He was very happy for me to treat the throat energy centre, which I did with some colour healing. Many radionic practitioners use the projection of colour in their radionic instruments, and the chakras or energy centres respond particularly well to this form of treatment. In this case, to open up the congested throat, I used the stimulating colour orange. In colour healing the reds and oranges are stimulating, while the blues, greens and darker shades act as a sedative. A few weeks of treatment on the colour instrument proved successful for my patient.

TREATING STRESS

In the scores of patients I treat radionically every month, stress is the predominant cause of symptoms like headaches, addictions (such as smoking and alcohol), weight gain and anxiety. No practitioner, whether orthodox or complementary, can change a patient's lifestyle. All we can do is give the patient tolerance of the situation, provide nutritional support for the physical body, and balance the patient's mental and emotional states, after identifying the cause of the stress.

This can be achieved by radionics. Analysing the patient's mental and emotional states and establishing the causes of deviation from perfection in these subtle body areas allows a more specific treatment to be administered (instead of just the 'hit or miss' approach of giving an anti-depressant or anti-anxiety drug).

Anxiety, depression, despondency and despair are common conditions suffered in the modern Western world, as we all strive to make ends meet materially and still endeavour to find some inner peace and tranquillity. A certain amount of stress can be beneficial, providing a stimulus to action. But too much will often result in anxiety (which can be defined as fear or apprehension not caused by real or apparent danger). Clinically, anxiety arises when the balance between certain chemicals in the brain is disturbed. The feelings of fear increase brain activity, stimulating the sympathetic nervous system, which in turn triggers physical symptoms such as shaking, palpitations, breathlessness, digestive disturbance and headaches.

Orthodox doctors will usually prescribe anti-anxiety drugs called anxiolytics or minor tranquillisers. These are used to alleviate the persistent feelings of nervousness and tension caused by stress or other psychological problems, but they cannot resolve the causes of the stress. Doctors will also prescribe anti-depressants along with Beta-blockers, and in cases of persistent insomnia sleeping drugs will be prescribed. However, it is vitally important to tackle the underlying cause, and this is best done through counselling or radionic analysis. Homeopathic medicine, along with Dr Bach Flower Remedies, can also offer relief and in some cases will address the causes.

Patients suffering anxiety will feel at times that their personal life is always fraught with difficulties. They often experience inner conflict, of an emotional nature, and sometimes at a business level, and this will cause more than normal levels of stress and trauma. Most of us, at some time or other, experience events that cause radical changes in our lives. They may seem unwelcome at first, yet these events will often clear the way forward, after the initial period of inner conflict. The emergence from inner conflict, whether experienced within oneself or externally with others, often coincides with the removal of outdated or superfluous aspects in life, thus allowing the individual to move forward unhindered into the future.

The radionic and subtle body assessment and analysis will check all areas of the subtle anatomy (see pages 86–7). Stress mainly affects the base of spine energy centre and the brow. These two centres are linked by meridians, and each of these meridians is numbered 1 to 20. These energy meridians carry the thought forms, attitudes and attributes that energise the chakras or energy centres controlling the glandular system of the body. After a radionic assessment or analysis is completed the practitioner will be able to identify more accurately the type of stress that has caused the patient's symptoms to manifest.

Not long ago I treated a typical stress case. The patient was complaining of tiredness, excess weight, backache and headaches and had recently given up smoking. I successfully treated him with radionics, using the biophoton radionic instrument on the subtle body only, and wrote to him as follows:

> There is a direct link between your hypertension and the tiredness with the tendency to being overweight. The overwork and stress was probably the reason for the start of the hypertension and the smoking was the outlet for the stress. Since the cessation of the smoking your body has been dealing with the stress by an overactive adrenal function and now the adrenal glands have become exhausted. The glands produce excess adrenalin in the form of a molecule called epinephrine when stress levels are high and continuous and the radionic assessment I have completed via the hair sample shows this to be the case.
>
> This adrenal molecule, when in excess, becomes toxic to the body when not burnt off by active exercise, the body then protects itself by creating thermogenesis (internal heat) to eradicate the harmful molecule. At the same time the body uses free potassium in the blood to tag the molecules and excrete them from the body, causing tiredness, bad nerves and water retention. This effect from the lowered

potassium causes excess sodium molecules, and the sodium chloride attracts water. Hence the patient puts on weight, and the stress increases.

More water in the blood causes the blood pressure to rise. Therefore we have now arrived at the complete picture and reason for all your symptoms: the interaction between the adrenal molecule created through stress and the depletion of elemental balance affecting the fluids of the body and the quality of the central nervous system.

I cannot change your lifestyle to eradicate the stress, but what I can do is provide you with natural remedies and supplements to give you far more tolerance of your environmental stress so the effects are far less. The weight will begin to reduce, the tension in the nervous system will ease, the blood pressure will reduce, and you will experience more energy.

My proposed treatment will be [automatically programmed] daily radionic projections for one month, reducing to every other day for the following month. The treatment will be given via the same hair sample used for the assessment and will comprise projections to reduce the overactive base of spine area and the adrenal function, along with a calming influence over the brow to reduce headaches. The overall projections will be designed to remove the cause of all your physical symptoms.

The patient reported to me regularly and after the two-month course of treatment felt he could cope with life more easily and there was no more craving for cigarettes. This was another case of treating the unseen areas of the subtle body. And this patient took no other form of medication, orthodox or complementary.

This also shows the efficacy of explaining to patients that certain stresses can cause physical symptoms. This understanding causes their conscious mind to affect their subconscious, thus speeding up the healing process.

TREATING ENERGY FIELDS

In 1985 an elderly but very fit-looking gentleman walked into my office with a slight limp and announced himself as a lieutenant colonel (retired) from the last world war.

He settled himself down in a chair, leant back and promptly swung one leg up onto my desk, proclaiming at the same time that he had heard that radionics could do wonders for the unseen energies of the human body. I nodded and was about to say a few words when he rolled up his trouser leg, fiddled with a couple of straps, took off his leg and placed it on the desk.

'That's the problem,' he said, pointing to the wooden leg now balanced in front of me.

'Bloody pain is intolerable.'

I immediately warmed to this rather eccentric character. We discussed the tragic event that had occurred during the war – a landmine had exploded beneath him and taken off his foot and part of the leg, which had been amputated above the knee.

'That's where it actually hurts,' he said, pointing to a spot below the arch of his artificial foot; on the base of the foot was a large cross drawn in blue felt-tip pen. He explained that the pain was intolerable under the foot at that point when the limb was attached to his upper leg. When the artificial leg was removed, as it was when he explained the symptoms, he pointed to a spot in thin air where his own foot used to be.

He told me it hurt a great deal, and that consultants, surgeons, doctors and healers had all attempted to relieve the pain of the phantom foot but to no avail. He looked at me with a wry smile: 'It's up to you now, Doc. Radionics is the only thing I haven't tried. Please see if you can help me. I can't take pain-killers for a pain that doesn't exist ...' I took a sample of hair and completed the case history, and the memorable colonel left.

I was unsure what approach to take in my radionic analysis of this unusual case, but I decided to start, as usual, by checking the readings for the physical body, then the readings of the energy centres and the mental and emotional states. All the main centres gave slight deviations which were of little concern to this patient's general state of health – no clues yet to the cause of the intolerable pain. I checked the skeletal system and the spine and also took readings on the minor centres of the feet, which are smaller electromagnetic fields related to the lymphatic system. To my astonishment, I found that I obtained readings for both the right and left foot. But this patient had no left foot.

The sudden realisation brought a smile to my face. The lieutenant colonel had clearly suffered an enormous emotional shock at the time of the explosion. The landmine had torn off the leg physically and severely damaged the energy field around the physical body, but the aura or etheric level of the leg and foot still remained intact, and was affirmed every time the colonel pointed to his leg. Clearly, all I had to do was remove the etheric field of energy around the phantom leg.

I set up an instrument with the basic command: remove the physical, etheric and emotional field of energy of the missing leg and disconnect that field from the patient's main energy fields. This I did by inserting standard Rae cards, and two that I had designed specifically for the projection, in the instrument slots. I then placed the hair sample in the instrument and switched on.

Within an hour the telephone rang: 'I don't know what you have done, Doc, but for the first time in I don't know how many years the pain has suddenly gone.' It had worked; the field of energy continuously transmitting the pain to the nervous system of his body had been interrupted by the radionic command.

However, this fascinating case had no real conclusion, as another factor soon appeared. After some pain-free months, the lieutenant colonel flew to Canada to visit his married son and as soon as the plane took off the pain in the phantom leg returned with the same intensity as before. This happened whenever he flew. After every flight he would call me, I would complete a treatment, and the pain would disappear, only to return again after flying.

I could find no reason for this and could only speculate that something occurred within this patient's energy fields due to changes in the gravitational forces and his own relationship to the earth's polarity when at altitude in an aeroplane. I treated him successfully about three times a year, which he really appreciated until his peaceful passing about five years ago. And this brings us to another aspect of radionic healing: dying with dignity.

TREATING THE DYING

In my opinion, keeping patients alive at all costs should not be the main criterion in healthcare and healing. Medical science often places the prolonging of life above all else, irrespective of the wishes of patients and family. But we all have to leave this world at some time; this inevitability should encourage medicine to bring peace, harmony and dignity to the treatment of the dying, rather than the over-use of powerful drugs and equipment to extend the transition period between life and death.

The moment of leaving the body should be peaceful and serene and infinitely more tranquil than the stress and pain of birth. There is of course the natural sadness and grief that accompanies the passing of a loved one. But in radionics we have special procedures to help the terminally ill, bringing inner peace and tranquillity, and removing the anguish from the transition. The treatments used vary from projections via the hair sample to high-potency homeopathic remedies made up on radionic simulation instruments.

Many times I have been told by relatives that their loved one passed over with a smile, no pain or distress, just turned their head and passed away. This enables the relatives to then celebrate the transition and look upon the passing life with gratitude and acknowledgement of the wonderful part that person played in their own lives.

Chapter 7

Radionics and Animals

A NIMALS RESPOND PARTICULARLY well to radionics for several reasons. Firstly, they always want to be well and, although they show individuality and a particular personality, they do not carry all the emotional baggage we humans haul around with us all the time. Animals also love unconditionally and therefore have very few blockages to their subtle anatomy and their emotions, apart from those emotions obtained from their interactions with humans. They are therefore very open to receiving radionic healing.

I continually hear the critics of radionics stating that the whole process of radionic analysis and treatment is contained within the patient's own belief system. They think that they will get well, so the mind assists the physical process of renewed wellbeing – i.e. it's all in the mind. My question to those cynics is, where do animals fit into this theory? Animals are not aware of the radionic procedures and the treatment of their own hair sample to restore their health. One could conceivably argue for the surrogate influence of owners over their pets, but then how do you explain the successful treatment of wild animals?

WILD ANIMALS

For many years my wife Chrissie and I lived in a cottage on Good Friday Hill at Godshill in Hampshire. Pine trees and rhododendrons grew on the hillside and we often watched wild foxes at play with their young and, at times (much to our surprise), with our own domestic cats.

One year we witnessed a decline in the activity of the fox family. They were less inclined to eat the food scraps that we put out for them, and they became emaciated animals with bald patches of red, raw skin. Sure enough they had developed fox mange.

One day Chrissie went out to a particular spot on the hill, where a vixen had been spotted vehemently scratching, and collected some samples of her hair. She placed the hairs between two sticky labels and positioned it on the radionic instrument and treatment was set up for fox mange. Chrissie treated the sample three or four times a day using the special radionic rate she had dowsed. In addition she projected the calming influence of Bach Flower Remedies and the vibration of homeopathic sulphur.

Within three weeks the fox clan began eating again, their fur began growing and they all put on weight. Radionics had healed the fox mange. All of the foxes had recovered by treating just one, using something that we know exists in the world of wild animals – group consciousness.

Chrissie also collected a fallen feather from a wild pheasant, with a severely damaged leg, that was a regular visitor to the garden. She treated the feather using radionics and in addition added homeopathic remedies and supplements to the feed she put out daily for the wild pheasants. Within a week the previously disfigured pheasant was once again 'strutting his stuff'.

PETS AND DOMESTIC ANIMALS

It seems bizarre that it is permissible to practise factory farming, and to inflict incredible cruelty on animals, supposedly for the benefit of medical research, yet it is against the law for anyone other than a veterinary surgeon to treat an animal. An animal owner cannot even treat their own pet when it is unwell and, according to the Veterinary Surgeons Act of 1966, owners face a stiff fine if found using any unorthodox methods such as radionics. Yet many enlightened veterinary surgeons use radionics as a diagnostic tool and means of treating animals. Chrissie receives regular referrals from veterinary surgeons and is privileged to treat the domestic animals and horses owned by the Royal family.

Our pets and domestic animals all live in the same environment as we do and are generally exposed to the same environmental pollutants, chemicals, microwave energies, processed and sub-standard foods. Not surprisingly, illness amongst our pets is increasing – to the extent that insurance cover is becoming a must (and not just for emergencies and accidents). Yet the natural therapies that support humans in their illnesses will work just as easily for the animals, both large and small. Although we humans stand erect, communicate with the spoken word and have developed our mental powers of logic and creativity rather more than our animal friends, the physical differences between human and animal biology are pretty insignificant. There is, however, one significant area of difference: animals, in particular wild animals, have developed and perfected their right brain function for use in perception and intuition. They use this for sensing their whereabouts in migration and for seeking their prey.

When assessing and treating animals radionically information can be gathered about the animal's health by the use of instruments and recordable readings obtained from the hair sample. Often there may be no apparent symptoms, and the animal obviously cannot tell you where it hurts. In such cases radionics can play a vital role.

TREATING ANIMALS RADIONICALLY

It is well-known that animals have a herd instinct and group consciousness that appears to be governed by instantaneous mental communication. What affects one will have an immediate impact upon the others, no matter how many animals in the herd, and no matter what time constraints are involved. For example, a flock of sparrows will all leave the ground instantly when startled. One does not influence another alongside it. There is no 'first one, then another, and another' sequence. It seems that animals are mentally attuned to one another and are not controlled by individual emotions, and this has fascinating implications for radionic veterinary practice.

Chrissie has been treating animals for the last eighteen years using homeopathy and radionics and has proven this with cattle. Where there are many animals together of the same breed, such as a dairy herd with many suffering mastitis, or the foxes I mentioned at the beginning of the chapter, we treat just one animal on the radionic instrument and the one sample and all the sick animals get better! This also applies to domestic pets in the home. Where two or three dogs have an infection, for example, the group consciousness appears to have dominion. And Chrissie has even known it happen with a flock of budgerigars in an aviary.

Over the years Chrissie has had a number of interesting animal patients. One case was a mare who displayed handling difficulties, particularly when being ridden favouring one side above the other. The owner strongly suspected a back or neck problem, but a veterinary examination found no evidence of this. Her hooves were also checked and were found to be sound.

Chrissie conducted a radionic assessment of the whole skeletal system via a hair sample submitted by the owner. She concluded that there was severe abnormality of the mandible joint and some faulty dentition. These problems were causing facial neuralgia and referred pain from the facial bones. Chrissie prescribed three weeks of radionic projection via the hair sample to correct the misalignment of the jawbones, along with treatment to reduce the inflammation and the use of a homeopathic remedy given orally. Tolerance remedies were also administered, whilst the radionics was being conducted. The mare made a full recovery after two months of radionic and oral remedy treatment.

Another amazing case that Chrissie treated

successfully involved a horse with a severe sarcoid. (This is a growth, often in the shape of a mushroom, that exudes from the skin of the animal; most unpleasant for horse and owner.) Conventional medicine had already been used – in the form of surgery, radiation and powerful medication – to no avail.

Once the radionic treatment started, it actually took many months to disable the viral causative factor and to eliminate the toxins from the horse's body. In order to speed up the healing process, oral nutritional supplements were given to support the animal's general constitution and immune system. The radionic treatment was given via the hair sample on a daily basis, using numerical rates to negate the viral infection and to promote immune response.

In this case the conventional diagnosis was accepted and radionics was used to ascertain the most favourable treatment. There has been no recurrence of the sarcoid for four years.

In humans the energy centres influence the activity of the glands and organ systems of the body, and so it is with animals. However, the treatment of animals with radionics does require additional knowledge. Radionic practitioners must have a good understanding of the systems of energy centres and meridians that vary according to each species.

Horses in particular have many and varied energy centres along their spine and chest that influence the performance of their physical body. This allows them considerable perception that appears to be linked to the enlightened rider. The treatment of the horse with the mandible joint symptoms required the treatment of special head energy centres that only exist in horses. In our practice, we often conduct radionic assessment and treatment for both horse and rider to obtain maximum communication and performance.

Similarly, dogs have special energy centres that exist in their paws. These influence their sensing abilities and give certain breeds greater perception and competence in tracking.

When it comes to dogs, radionics is also very successful. Many cases involve skin and coat problems, with severe loss of hair and skin irritation which the poor animal scratches red raw. Often the vet's answer is to put a neck collar on the animal to prevent it scratching. Can you imagine anything worse than having a severe irritation and not being able to scratch it?! These problems are frequently caused by annual vaccinations that present a continuous challenge to the animal's immune system, and the immediate treatment should be directed at the immune system.

DEALING WITH PESTS

Amazingly, Chrissie and I spent many years treating banana plantations in Ecuador, South

America, from the comfort of our offices in Hampshire. We were sent soil samples, aerial photographs and plant details and set up a radionic treatment plan that was operational twenty-four hours a day. We were given the names of all the pests known to love bananas and we made special cards and developed rates to treat them.

The whole programme went very well until it became clear that the owner was obtaining a higher yield than his neighbours and questions were asked as to what was going on. The farm was eventually sold and the new owners could not 'comprende' what radionics from England had to do with the banana yield, so that was the end of our contract. In fact radionics is very effective in treating plants and soil as well as pests. For those who are interested in treating plants with radionics the Radionic Association of Great Britain (see Useful Addresses) has a division or register of radionic practitioners qualified in agriculture.

Another good radionic pest story dates back to the 1980s when David Tansley and I were living on the country estate of the late Dr Aubrey Westlake at Godshill. We were often visited by doctors and other healthcare professionals, many of whom came from overseas. One of these visiting doctors, Ed (who was also a homeopath and reiki practitioner), was from Canada.

Much of the land overlooking the Avon

valley was given over to camping and holiday
lodges. That particular summer all the accommodation was full, so Ed took a room at a bed and
breakfast about half a mile up the road and would
walk down to my office each day for the lectures.

It was one of those rare dry English summers,
and the woodland lodges and the camping areas in
the open fields became infested with earwigs, a
small insect with pincers at the end of its body. If
these little creatures get in your sleeping bag or
you sit on them on the grass you suddenly feel a
painful nip and they hold on for dear life as you try
to brush them off your skin. The dry weather had
encouraged thousands of them to invade the
holiday centre – to the point where Dr Westlake's
son Richard, the estate manager, (knowing about
radionics) summoned help.

Customers were leaving the site and demanding refunds, as they could not cope with the
infestation. 'Could radionics come to the rescue?',
enquired Richard? I said I would need a map or an
aerial photograph of the estate and the area
infested and one of the offending earwigs (alive, in
a matchbox). These Richard provided, and
Chrissie and I set to work.

Because God's creatures are all on this planet
for a reason, when nature does get their numbers
and habitat wrong it is usually due to human
mishandling of the environment. But, whatever
the reason for the glut of earwigs, they had to be
removed away from the holiday centre. Chrissie

dowsed with the pendulum over a rate-type radionic instrument at a frequency to which the live earwig reacted violently. I then let it go free, as, although Chrissie loves nature, there are some things she refuses to pick up! After this I took the area of the infestation marked on the photograph, placed it on a vertical plate, and then projected the selected rate over the denoted area.

I added to this a further instruction that earwigs should live in the forest half a mile or so up the road. This was in the form of a special card and I linked this command to the rate projection instrument. The special card I made was a numerical equivalent of a written instruction to move to their natural habitat. (This can be done in radionics by converting the written word to a series of numbers, as in numerology.) I then switched the system on, hoping to encourage the earwigs to leave the estate; this was a Monday morning.

Meanwhile, Ed from Canada had arrived on the preceding Sunday. He told me on the Monday morning that his accommodation at the B & B was perfect and he was looking forward to his first week of lectures.

Nothing happened at the estate in regard to the marauding earwigs on the Monday or Tuesday so I left the radionic projection pulsing away. I told Richard to be patient, as he came to report to me three times a day about how many holidaymakers had left with their refunds.

On Wednesday, Ed arrived for the morning

lecture scratching and itching, at just the same moment as Richard walked into my office. He was elated that no more earwigs could be seen.

'No,' said Ed. 'They are all at the B & B half a mile up the road. I have been eaten alive all night and the guests are all demanding refunds.'

That's the magic of radionics!

Chapter 8

Energy Medicine Born Out of Radionics

POSSIBLY ONE OF THE MOST baffling things about biological organisms, from the microscopic to the macroscopic (and we humans fit somewhere in between), is their teleological quality – in other words, the possible existence of a causal element that provides an ultimate purpose in their development. In the case of humans, we have the will to live from the very beginning (that point after the pronuclei fuse at conception), through gestation, birth, maturity and finally the death of the physical body. At every stage, there has to be a reason and a plan to life.

RADIONICS AND ANCIENT TEACHINGS

When I first came into contact with Dr Aubrey Westlake, David Tansley and Lavender Dower I noticed that they incorporated many traditional philosophies in their radionic practice. This encouraged me to look at some of these ancient philosophical teachings more closely. I had already found similarities between many traditional forms of medicine and teachings and even a connection to modern science and biology. I knew there had to be a way of pulling the various strands of knowledge together to form a dependable foundation on which to build a medicine for the future.

I had already observed that in biology the blueprint of life was only created when male sperm and female egg joined to form the first cell of human life. After this fusion of the pronuclei, thirty-two cells were required (each with a positive and negative electrical charge) to divide once more before implantation on the uterine wall could occur. This appeared to indicate that sixty-four was a very significant number.

Interestingly, there are sixty-four hexagrams in the *I-Ching* (the Chinese Book of Changes), which is widely regarded as a guide to the interpretation of living consciousness, demonstrating the link between spiritual and physical life. Each hexagram is made up of six broken or unbroken lines in a unique configuration, and each one represents a specific concept relating to nature and human interaction.

The Hebrew word *Qabalah* means 'to

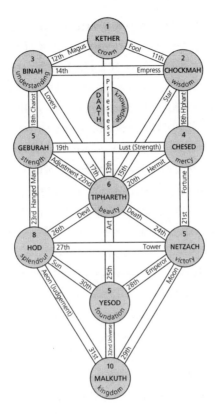

Figure 12 The Qabalistic Tree of Life.

receive and reveal'. This ancient teaching is based on a diagram known as 'the tree of life' (see Figure 12). It shows ten spheres connected by twenty-two pathways, and – when fully under-stood – offers a unique system of personal exploration and development. The ten spheres and twenty-two pathways all have both positive and negative polarity, as knowledge flows in both directions on all the interconnecting pathways. Again we have the magical sixty-four.

In radionics David Tansley interpolated the philosophies of traditional texts from China, India and Ancient Greece that referred to invisible bodies and chakra systems, with the then Western system of radionics (as explained in Chapter 2). The chakras are similar to the spheres in the tree of life and there are, again, twenty-two pathways between them. The energy flow in the pathways is multi-directional and relates to the positive and negative thoughts that can be exchanged between the chakras. Again, the magical sixty-four raises its head.

In modern radionics ten chakras are used. The tenth centre or chakra is non-physical in its manifestation and is not used in radionic philosophy when dealing with physical, mental or emotional health. It is called Daarth, and has a role in the birthing and passing of life. For more on this, readers can refer to my book *Medicine for the 21st Century* (see Further Reading), which gives a full explanation of its role esoterically and in particular in relation to birth and death.

MEDICINE FOR THE 21ST CENTURY

These interconnections between traditional knowledge and modern medicine fascinated me for years. Then one day an event occurred that sowed a seed in my mind, a seed that would eventually grow into *Medicine for the 21st Century*.

This experience occurred in the latter part of the 1980s.

Chrissie and I had practised for many years at the Institute for Complementary Medicine in Portland Place in London. The Institute attracted many eminent visitors from overseas, including several doctors, one of whom became interested in radionics. Roberto was from Mexico City and he invited Chrissie and me to visit a few of his medical friends in Mexico and speak about radionics. We agreed at the time and then thought no more about it, as six months went by without us hearing from him again. Then, out of the blue, two airline tickets arrived from Roberto, with open-ended dates. We did not take long to pack. In fact we were soon on our way, as it was February and England was very grey and cold.

We duly arrived in Mexico City. It was fairly late when we reached the hotel and so we decided to get a good night's rest before the seminar the next morning. After breakfast we sauntered down to the foyer to look for Roberto and his friends, and noticed a placard saying 'Keith Mason Radionic Seminar in the Crystal Room'. We furtively entered to find over 120 doctors and professionals, all wearing headphones, and three translators at the back of the room sitting in small booths with their translation books at the ready. These were Roberto's few medical friends!

We actually enjoyed the four days of lectur-ing, but the high point of the trip was our visit to

Roberto's clinic on the outskirts of the city. The queues formed from early morning, Roberto told us as we drew up at the clinic and witnessed the smiling faces awaiting him. For the first time in my life I saw a true doctor who based his healing art upon Western medical training alongside ancient knowledge passed down from his Mayan forebears.

Here was a doctor who could tell his patients what was actually wrong with them; they did not say a word. At the initial consultation with each patient Roberto looked at the card completed by the secretary at reception. The card listed only name, date of birth, where the patient was born, etc. (just ten pieces of information were given). The patient sat quietly in front of Roberto whilst he looked at them intently. He then turned to his desk where an impressive circular chart was lying. There were circles within circles; each one revolved and each individual ring was inlaid with traditional inscriptions.

Roberto looked at the patient's card, made adjustments to the various circles and then spoke to the patient, saying, for example, 'Today you have come to see me because of your stomach. A week ago you experienced a severe worry with a business colleague and had much stress and your bowels are now very congested. Your appetite is poor and now your skin is erupting.'

The patient just said, 'Yes, doctor, you are quite right, thank you.'

He gave the patient a prescription and told them to see the nurse on the way out. The whole procedure took no more than five minutes.

This doctor could look at a patient, twiddle some rather large dials on his circular chart, and make a completely accurate diagnosis of symptoms and the cause of those symptoms without the patient saying a word. Chrissie and I expressed our amazement in no uncertain terms.

'This is not amazing,' he said. 'This is radionics with a slight difference. I do not use a pendulum. It's just traditional knowledge encased in this medicine wheel. Look, it works with a combination of sixty-four symbols.'

Radionics without a pendulum – something I had spoken of years before to the Radionic Association when I had first thought about combining traditional knowledge with Western medicine and, of course, physics. The spark within me was ignited, and the book was written in the next few years. The Base Sixty-Four System of radionics was also planted and has now grown into a branch of radionics known as energy medicine.

ASSESSMENT THROUGH KNOWLEDGE

Medicine for the 21st Century was essentially written for my students of radionics. The system described in the book has now been turned into a computer program which incorporates elements of numerology, cosmology, the Qabalah, and Chinese and Tibetan philosophy. The information a patient provides on the case history is entered into the computer and a report is provided, giving the practitioner detailed information about the inherited and formative activity from birth of all the chakras (or energy centres). This information is compared to the symptoms the patient has indicated on the completed case history and the practitioner can then identify the possible causes of those symptoms.

This system of energy medicine is basically radionics without the use of a pendulum, which, as I have already mentioned, is very attractive to doctors and other healthcare professionals. Here is an example of the type of report a Base Sixty-Four computer program might provide for a patient suffering from headaches, tiredness and skin problems. No hair sample is required; the patient simply submits a completed case history and receives the following report from the computer program which I personally edit for ease of understanding:

> In your case the cause of the headache, the stomach-ache with nausea, the skin condition and the constant tiredness are related to two main areas. These are the digestion and the liver in particular and the adrenal gland function. What I find, through the assessment

programme, is that both the liver and adrenal gland functions are weak due to certain stresses that affect these two organs in particular.

Certain stress of a particular nature (which I will expand upon) will affect the way nutrients are absorbed from your diet. A lack of specific nutrients will cause organs and endocrine glands to have poor metabolic rates, which will interfere with their performance in the body. In your case potassium is lacking, along with magnesium, and is causing the internal digestive problems and related headaches, but in particular the potassium loss is the cause of the tiredness and the skin condition.

Eczema, although a long-term problem, is also related to the weakness of potassium in your body since childhood. The reason for the stomach-ache and slight nausea is the vagus nerve which controls the nervous actions of the stomach and is again affected by low-level, but long-term stress. This you may find difficult to accept, as you appear to be very easygoing and laid-back in your personality according to your completed case history. However, the assessment and mineral profile I have conducted throws more light on the condition.

The computer assessment shows you to be a very caring, understanding, logical and discriminating person with accuracy in your dealings with other people. You have a great love of colour and the beautiful things in life, both from the material and the natural world. You base your life upon traditional family values and when faced with anxiety or worries will use both logic and intuitive thinking to solve the problem. These are the strengths of your character and personality, but we all have weaknesses that we have to address and in your case these small weaknesses are creative of the low-level and inner stresses that you suffer, and perhaps do not speak of to others.

Because of your caring abilities and your understanding of the needs of others you often allow yourself to be manipulated by the strong convictions of others. You hate argument and discord and will do anything to avoid altercation, but there are times when you feel the need to speak your mind but are disinclined, as you do not wish to hurt the feelings of others. The stress you suffer comes from inner frustration due to your own willpower being overruled at times and the lack of resolve in 'saying it as it is'. You should really speak your mind and be more wilful in what you wish to do.

This type of inner stress causes poor potassium metabolism in the body and will lead to headaches, stomach-ache and the other symptoms you detail in your case history. Your adrenal glands will produce excess adrenal hormones. The body recognises these as toxic and will remove them from your bloodstream by tagging the hormone with potassium molecules, causing yet another lowering of potassium levels.

My proposed treatment is a couple of months on a programme of specific pharmaceutical grade supplements to correct the potassium/magnesium imbalances and a homeopathic remedy for your general constitution.

I then send the patient a covering note detailing the dosages of the supplements and remedies with a request for a progress report after a month. The report specifies the elemental minerals required to overcome the problems, along with energetic remedies such as Dr Bach Flower Remedies and homeopathic remedies.

RADIONICS AND OTHER THERAPIES

As an energy medicine, radionics is favoured by practitioners of many other therapies as an adjunct to their own diagnostic procedures. (However, radionics can itself ascertain the causes of illness and should not be used purely as a complement to orthodox diagnosis and treatment.) Over many years of practice and teaching, I have come into contact with doctors, dentists, acupuncturists and chiropractors who all use radionics as a diagnostic tool, as well as for treatment and the making up of oral remedies.

Dentistry

Both in analysis and treatment procedures radionic practitioners have at their disposal rate books and reference cards for all the teeth and their components as well as information on the general wellbeing of the oral cavity. Radionic analysis will often identify a focal point of inflammation or root canal or bridge-work as being responsible for symptoms occurring in the physical body, causing a non-local effect. For example, a root canal or filling can be a toxic influence on the nervous system, which can then pollute the bloodstream or bone system. A radionic practitioner will often include analysis of the teeth as a routine part of their overall assessment of a new patient.

In Great Britain the International Academy of Oral Medicine and Toxicology (see Useful Addresses) promotes holistic dentistry. Many dental surgeons belonging to the group use radionics; I know this to be true as I have taught them how to use the instruments myself. Indeed, one of my own patients recently called me, whilst on holiday in Scotland, to say that she was, 'in agony with a back tooth'. She explained that they were miles from a large town and begged me to see what I could do for her.

I took her hair sample from the file, checked radionically and found major deviations from perfection in a lower left bicuspid; not quite a back tooth but obviously causing considerable pain to the patient as it spread around the side of the mouth. I used the reference card for the colour blue and linked this with an identification card for the lower left bicuspid–5 and a further instruction to remove inflammation. I used a biophoton instrument which fires light photons through the cards and into a reflective chamber where I placed the patient's hair sample.

Later that evening she rang me to say the pain had eased and to please keep the radionic projection going, which I duly did until she returned a few days later. She made an appointment with the local dentist who confirmed the deterioration of an amalgam filling in the bicuspid and it was restored with porcelain.

Many of my patients ask me for a yearly health check-up, and specifically request a radionic dental check.

Radionics and chiropractors

The late David Tansley was the most prolific writer on the subject of radionics and he was an honours graduate from the Los Angeles College of Chiropractic in 1965. Chiropractors, in the USA particularly, recognise the need for the correct energy balance over the whole spinal column. One herniated disk or misalignment can cause havoc throughout the body, often affecting the nervous energy flowing to an organ system, and thus resulting in physical symptoms. Because radionics is an energy medicine it works well with the spinal column and is useful for correcting vertebrae when they are out of alignment.

Special radionic instruments exist, along with reference cards for treating spinal conditions, and chiropractors use these in conjunction with their own manipulative techniques. One of the attractions for chiropractors (as for dental surgeons) is that patients can be treated in emergency conditions without actually attending the practice. And, for patients, radionic chiropractic adjustment is a lot less painful than the normal version!

Radionics and acupuncture

The Chinese name for the cyclic energy that flows through the meridians or pathways of the body is *chi*. This energy has to flow freely for health to be maintained in the physical body. When blockages occur for various reasons the flow of *chi* can be stimulated by needles inserted at special points along the meridians.

The workings of the meridians and the respective acupuncture points have been documented over thousands of years, and are based upon the Chinese philosophy of continuous cyclic rhythms, which are fundamental to the whole universe. Many acupuncturists use radionics to stimulate or calm particular points. They can do this by using the hair sample in a treatment instrument with the reference cards or rates set up on the instrument to treat the points in question.

Electrical, magnetic or light photon instruments can all have their pulsation adjusted to stimulate or sedate an acupuncture point. And all this work can be accomplished at a distance, with the acupuncturist's patient being either miles away or in the adjoining room.

Chapter 9

Radionics and the Probability of Success

JUST AS THE ELECTRONIC REACTION of Abrams (ERA) was one of the most revolutionary medical breakthroughs in the early part of the twentieth century, radionics is more than likely to put the cat amongst the pigeons yet again – probably within the next decade. Back in the early 1900s, when the ERA was discovered, medical practice was adopting the mechanistic model of the human body and starting to use 'miracle' chemical drugs to treat it. The dream of discovering wonder drugs to cure all diseases has not been fulfilled. Rather the opposite has occurred, with an increase in the number of illnesses caused by inappropriate use of drugs and their insidious side-effects. According to some estimates, these iatrogenic illnesses account for more than 25 per cent of all hospital admissions.

There is a rapidly growing interest in alternative and complementary medicine, which in time will force orthodoxy to reconsider its approach to other healing methods. Already some healing professions are affiliated to orthodox medical practice and patients can take out medical insurance to cover the costs of such alternative treatments. Modern radionics uses procedures that many orthodox physicians certainly feel are very revolutionary. And radionics has an ace up its sleeve or (to put it another way, as radionics is theoretically linked to quantum physics), it has a proverbial 'jack' in the probability radionic box.

Let me explain a theoretical or imaginary experiment referred to in quantum mechanics as 'ghostly electrons-in-the-box' experiment. I have already given examples of treating areas of the unseen which have an effect upon the physical body. I have spoken of the atoms and electrons that make up the human body and written about fields of force used in treatment procedures. Well, here is another experiment concerning the nature of reality. It is similar to the EPR experiment (which showed thought travelling huge distances in an instant), but this concerns the *probability* of what could happen; it all depends upon the observer and what you want to happen. Remember that 'the observer' referred to in physics is akin to the 'practitioner' in radionic assessment or treatment.

The probability experiment brings out clearly the role of the observer in determining what happens in the unseen world of atoms and electrons that make up the visible, material world. The simplest example is to imagine a box containing a single electron. If nobody looks in the box, then, according to the standard interpretation of what goes on in the quantum world (known as the Copenhagen Interpretation), there is an equal probability of finding the electron anywhere inside the box. (This interpretation is the work of physicist Niels Bohr from Copenhagen – hence the name.)

Imagine that, still without anyone looking, a partition is automatically lowered into the middle of the box, dividing it into two equal boxes. Common sense tells us that the electron must be in one side of the box or the other. But the Copenhagen Interpretation tells us that the probability wave is still evenly distributed across both half-boxes. That means there is a 50:50 chance of finding the electron in *either* side of the box. The probability wave controlling the electron only collapses, with the electron becoming 'real', when somebody looks into the boxes and notices on which side of the partition the electron is.

The choice of which side to look in first is unimportant. At the actual moment of observation, when the observer looks in one half of the box, the probability wave in the other half vanishes instantly. If you close up the box again, and stop looking for the electron, its probability wave spreads out once more to fill the half-box in which it was located by the observer and will not spread out into the other half-box.

This means that, prior to observation, there are two nebulous or indistinct 'ghostly' or 'spooky' electrons inhabiting each side of the box just waiting to be observed. When observation does take place the electron instantly becomes 'real', and simultaneously the other ghostly electron disappears completely. The importance of this quantum physics experiment with regard to radionics is that what you wish to observe as happening in the treatment instrument is 'real'. Because thought is the medium of transference, the EPR phenomenon (described in Chapter 3) causes the patient – however far away – to receive the effects instantly.

When treating patients with very serious illnesses my radionic treatment instrument is programmed to collapse the probability wave of the electrons around the atoms controlling diseased cells and to make real the electrons around the atoms controlling healthy cells. This form of radionic treatment is 'real' healing at a distance, taking place in the unseen world of the physics that controls the matter of the human body.

The probability wave comes into the picture once more, when the patient receives the healing thought forms from the practitioner and his instrument. However, the patient must be open to receiving the healing, because the probability wave controlling electrons can either become 'real' or collapse depending upon the patient (who is now the observer or receiver in the experiment). This is why the success of radionic healing depends upon the patient's intent to receive the healing. Their intent is actually the witness they send the practitioner in the form of the hair sample and the request for radionic treatment in the first place. This wave-form of probability must be intact before treatment can begin.

In fact this is true of all healing, whether orthodox or complementary. There has to be the desire to get well and a purpose to the life of the patient. Remember, each and every cell has a mind of its own and listens to your mind and moods all the time.

I personally believe it is very difficult for the body to develop illness. It has an innate longing for well-being and its cells constantly endeavour to maintain health, without our conscious intervention. Although many people experience genetic and inherited illness or malfunctions acquired at birth, there are in my opinion very few basic causes of ill-health. Even those unfortunate patients experiencing acquired or genetic malfunctions will gain a degree of improvement from some positive and corrective thinking, as thought is electrical and the cells of the body contain elemental compounds comprising elec-tromagnetic fields of force. The use of radionics in healing and treating these fields of force will not only improve the integrity of healthy cells and body structures but will also enhance the ability of malformed or genetically affected parts of the body to act in a more natural manner.

In addition, in order to create additional healthy immune cells to counteract the cells released by any malignant growth or degenerative illness, you must have a creative and active mind. Your physical body, comprising billions of cells, listens continually to your mental demands. If you are burdened by thoughts of despair and constant fear of a particular disease, your body will think the same, and its cells, each with a 'mind of its own', will act accordingly.

As my mentor, the late Dr Aubrey Westlake, so wisely said, 'All disease is curable, but not all patients.' Radionics is an extraordinarily effective healing art but its success still depends on the patient having *a purpose to life and the will to get better*.

Useful
Addresses

For training in radionics contact:

Keith Mason
Keith Mason School of Radionics
Old Stables, East Claydon
Buckinghamshire, MK18 2ND
E-mail: keithmason@dial.pipex.com

The Radionic Association
Baerlein House
Goose Green
Deddington, Banbury
Oxfordshire OX15 0SZ.
Tel: 01869 338852
Fax: 01869 338852
Website: www.radionic.co.uk
E-mail: secretary@radionic.co.uk

The Institute for Complementary Medicine
PO Box 194
London
SE16 7QZ.
Tel: 020 7237 5165
Fax: 020 7237 5175
E-mail: icm@icmedicine.co.uk

British Register of Complementary Practitioners
(radionics and energy medicine section)
PO Box 194
London
SE16 7QZ.
Website: www.brcp@icmedicine.co.uk

For information on holistic dentistry contact:

Dr Anthony Newbury
The International Academy of Oral Medicine
    and Toxicology
72 Harley Street
London
W1N 1AC.

For radionic analysis, assessment, health reports, teaching enquiries and appointments for consultations, write (enclosing a stamped addressed envelope) to:

Keith Mason
Old Stables
East Claydon
Buckinghamshire
MK18 2ND
E-mail: keithmason@dial.pipex.com

Dr Edward Bach Ltd
Mount Vernon
Bakers Lane
Sotwell
Wallingford
OX10 0PZ
Tel: 01491 825022
Fax: 01491 834678
Website: www.bachcentre.com

Further Reading

Augros, Robert and Stanciu, George, *The New Biology*, Random House.

Bailey, Alice, *Esoteric Psychology*, Volume Two, Lucis Press, 1942.

Davies, Paul, *The Cosmic Blueprint*, Touchstone, 1995.

Davies, Paul and Brown, Julian, *Superstrings*, Cambridge University Press, 1992.

Dower, Lavender, *Healing with Radionics*, Thorsons, 1980.

Mason, Keith, *Medicine for the 21st Century*, Element Books, 1992.

Mason, Keith, *Thoughts that Harm, Thoughts that Heal*, Piatkus, 2000.

Milner and Smart, *Loom of Creation*, Neville Spearman, 1975.

Russell, Edward W., *Report on Radionics*,

Neville Spearman, 1973.

Tansley, David, *Dimensions of Radionics*, C.W. Daniels, 1977.

Tansley, David, *Radionics: A Patient's Guide*, Element, 1985.

Tansley, David, *Subtle Anatomy of Man*, C.W. Daniels, 1972.

Westlake, Aubrey, *The Pattern of Health*, Element.

Index

Index

Thoughts That Harm, Thoughts That Heal

Overcoming common ailments through the power of your mind

by Keith Mason

Do you find your job literally 'a pain in the neck'? Does an irritating person 'get under your skin'? Conversely, when you share a problem, do you feel 'a weight has been lifted from your shoulders'? It has long been known that your state of mind affects your physical health. This life-changing new book will:

- Reveal that specific types of thoughts cause particular symptoms and ailments. For example backache can be associated with an unwillingness to face new challenges, while asthma can reflect communication difficulties.
- Show how you can use the power of your thoughts and attitudes to cure yourself, and improve and maintain your general health.
- Completely change the way you think about illness.
- Show that the key to good health lies within your own mind.

Keith Mason PhD has had over 30 years' experience in complementary medicine. He runs his own successful practice and lectures in the USA, Australia and around the world.

Vertical Reflexology

A revolutionary five-minute technique to transform your health

by Lynne Booth

In *Vertical Reflexology*, leading reflexologist Lynne Booth introduces a revolutionary approach to treating common ailments: Vertical Reflex Therapy. VRT works on the top of the feet while the patient is standing and provides amazing benefits. A clinical trial and feedback from practitioners and clients have shown that VRT:

- Provides deeper access to reflex points so that the treatment is quicker and more effective than conventional reflexology.
- Enhances and complements professional reflexology treatments.
- Achieves significant results in just 5 minutes.
- Provides access to many new reflex points including reflexes for stimulating the immune system and calf reflexes to help ease back pain and chest congestion.
- Makes it easier and more effective to treat yourself.

Vertical Reflexology features step-by-step illustrations, unique dorsal foot charts, treatment descriptions and outlines the key reflex points to treat a range of health problems. It is *the* essential guide to a major breakthrough in natural health care.

Lynne Booth runs a private reflexology practice in Bristol and practises reflexology at a residential nursing home. She regularly gives seminars in Britain and around the world, and is in demand internationally to provide training in VRT.

Vibrational Medicine for the 21st Century

A complete guide to energy healing and spiritual transformation

by Richard Gerber MD

Vibrational Medicine for the 21st Century is the definitive guide to energy healing, the most exciting new development in contemporary medicine. International expert Dr Richard Gerber explains the principles of energy medicine and answers your most commonly asked questions about major therapies such as acupuncture, flower essences and colour healing. In this ground-breaking book you will discover:

- The latest scientific research that confirms the healing wisdom of ancient cultures
- The power of thoughts and consciousness to transform health
- A user-friendly guide to homeopathy, acupuncture, flower essences, colour and light, magnet therapy, radionics and the laying-on of hands
- How each therapy works, the health problems they can treat most effectively, and what takes place during a typical visit to a practitioner

Both practical and inspirational, *Vibrational Medicine in the 21st Century* is the essential guide to this revolutionary approach to health.

Dr Richard Gerber practises internal medicine near his home in Livonia, Michigan, and has become the definitive authority for energetic medicine. He has researched alternative medicine for over twenty years and is a popular international teacher in the field. His first book, *Vibrational Medicine* sold over 100,000 copies.

Your Body Speaks Your Mind

Understand how your emotions affect your health

by Debbie Shapiro

This important new book reveals the intimate relationship which exists between your mind and your body.
Debbie Shapiro intuitively explains the way in which
your body reflects your thoughts and feelings and how
you can use this understanding for self healing.

In this inspiring book you will:

- Learn how your emotional and psychological states
  affect you physically
- Discover how your feelings and thoughts are linked
  to specific parts of the body and different illnesses
- Become aware of how unresolved issues affect your
  health and what is needed to being about your
  healing
- Find out how to use the power of your mind and
  heart to heal your body through creative visualisation, relaxation and meditation
- Discover how breath awareness, movement, and
  complementary healing techniques can stimulate
  emotional and psychological healing

Debbie Shapiro has spent over 20 years studying yoga,
psychology, bodymind language and Buddhist meditation. She is the author of *The Bodymind Workbook*, *A
Time for Healing* and several other books written with
her husband, Eddie, that deepen awareness of healing
through the mind, heart and body. They are both
respected spiritual teachers.

PIATKUS BOOKS

If you have enjoyed reading this book, you may be interested in other titles published by Piatkus. These include:

Afterlife, The: An investigation into the mysteries of life after death   Jenny Randles and Peter Hough

Balancing Your Chakras: How to balance your seven energy centres for health and wellbeing   Sonia Choquette

Barefoot Doctor's Handbook for Modern Lovers: A spiritual guide to truly amazing love and sex   Barefoot Doctor

Book of Shadows: A modern Witch reveals the wisdom of Witchcraft and the power of the Goddess   Phyllis Curott

Chakras: A new approach to healing your life   Ruth White

Changes: A guide to personal transformation and new ways of living in the new millennium   Soozi Holbeche

Channelling: What it is and how to do it   Lita de Alberdi

Children and the Spirit World: A book for bereaved families   Linda Williamson

Clear Your Clutter With Feng Shui   Karen Kingston

Colour Healing Manual: The complete colour therapy programme   Pauline Wills

Colours of the Soul: Transform your life through colour therapy   June McLeod

Complete Guide to Divination, The: How to use the most popular methods of fortune-telling   Cassandra Eason

Complete Guide to Psychic Development, A: Over 35 ways to tap into your psychic potential   Cassandra Eason

Creating Sacred Space With Feng Shui   Karen Kingston

Stepping into the Magic: A new approach to everyday life   Gill Edwards

Talking to Heaven: A medium's message of life after death   James Van Praagh

Teach Yourself to Meditate: Over 20 simple exercises for peace, health and clarity of mind   Eric Harrison

Thoughts That Harm, Thoughts That Heal: Overcoming common ailments through the power of your mind   Keith Mason

Time for Healing, A: The journey to wholeness   Eddie and Debbie Shapiro

Time for Transformation, A: How to awaken to your soul's purpose and claim your power   Diana Cooper

Transform Your Life: A step-by-step programme for change   Diana Cooper

Vibrational Medicine for the 21st Century: A complete guide to energy healing and spiritual transformation   Richard Gerber MD

Way of Harmony, The: How to find true abundance in your life   Jim Dreaver

Woman's Spiritual Journey, A: Finding the feminine path to fulfilment   Joan Borysenko

Working with Angels, Fairies and Nature Spirits   William Bloom

Working with Guides and Angels   Ruth White

Working with Your Chakras: An introduction to the energy centres of your body   Ruth White

Your Body Speaks Your Mind: Understand how your thoughts and emotions affect your health   Debbie Shapiro

Your Healing Power: A comprehensive guide to channelling your healing abilities   Jack Angelo

Your Heart's Desire: Using the language of manifestation to create the life you really want   Sonia Choquette

Your Mind's Eye: How to heal yourself and release your potential through creative visualisation   Rachel Charles